S0-AAA-173

K¹² Math⁺

Illustrations Credits
All illustrations © K12 Inc. unless otherwise noted

All photographs are royalty-free. © Artville, © Dreamstime.com,
© Fotolia, © K12 Inc., © iStockphoto.com

About K12 Inc.
K12 Inc., a technology-based education company, is the nation's leading provider of proprietary curriculum and online education programs to students in grades K–12. K^{12} provides its curriculum and academic services to online schools, traditional classrooms, blended school programs, and directly to families. K12 Inc. also operates the K^{12} International Academy, an accredited, diploma-granting online private school serving students worldwide. K^{12}'s mission is to provide any child the curriculum and tools to maximize success in life, regardless of geographic, financial, or demographic circumstances. K12 Inc. is accredited by CITA. More information can be found at www.K12.com.

Copyright © 2011, 2009 K12 Inc. All rights reserved. K^{12}, the K^{12} logo, and Unleash the xPotential are trademarks or registered trademarks of K12 Inc. or its affiliates in the U.S. and other countries. Other names may be trademarks of third parties.

No part of this document may be reproduced or used in any form or by any means, graphic, electronic, or mechanical, including photocopying, recording, taping, and information retrieval systems, without the prior written permission of K12 Inc.

ISBN: 978-1-60153-081-3
Printed by RR Donnelley, Shenzhen, China, March 2012, Lot 032012

Contents

Numbers Through 500

Time and Money

Add, Subtract, Number Composition

Inverse Operations: Add and Subtract

Measurement

Add or Subtract: Problem Solving

Problem Solving: Reason and Connect

Semester Review and Checkpoint

Numbers Through 1,000

Plane and Solid Figures

Add or Subtract Numbers Through 1,000

Multiplication and Number Patterns

Multiplication and Addition Properties

Introduction to Division

Data Representations and Analysis

Introduction to Fractions

Semester Review and Checkpoint

Semester Review

Printouts

    10-Section Spinner
    Fact Family Triangles
    Fraction Circles
    Horizontal Bar Graph
    Hundred Chart
    Hundred Grid
    Inch Grid Paper
    Multiplication Facts Chart
    My Story Problems
    Number Line 0–2
    Number Line 0–20
    Number Line 0–100
    Open Number Lines
    Paper Clock Model
    Picture Graph
    Place-Value Chart (Hundreds)
    Place-Value Chart (Thousands)
    Place-Value Mat – Thousands Column
    Vertical Bar Graph
    Whole to Twelfths Number Lines

Count Aloud Through 500

Let's Count!

Count aloud.

1. Count aloud from 126 to 146.

2. Count aloud from 294 to 302.

3. Count aloud from 387 to 405.

4. Count aloud from 100 to 200.

5. Pretend you are going to count from 300 to 400. Count for a few seconds. How does counting from 300 to 400 sound the same as counting from 100 to 200? How does it sound different?

TRY IT

6. Say the numbers in order from 185 to 205.

7. Say the numbers in order from 250 to 275.

8. Say the numbers in order from 480 to 490.

9. Say the numbers in order from 310 to 325.

10. Say the numbers in order from 290 to 305.

TRY IT

Read Whole Numbers Through 500

Read That Number!

Say each number. Place a check on the mailbox when you have finished.

127

12

255

472

340

399

406

111

225

210

460

334

103

212

500

T R Y   I T

1. What number is this?

   401

2. What number is this?

   278

3. What number is this?

   387

4. What number is this?

   123

5. Say these numbers aloud.

   345, 346, 347, 348, 349, 350, 351, 352

Write Numerals Through 500

Writing Numerals on Hundred Charts

Hundred Chart 1

					126	127	128	129	130
131	132	133	134	135	136	137	138	139	140
141	142	143	144	145	146	147	148	149	150
151	152	153	154	155	156	157	158	159	160
161	162	163	164	165	166	167	168	169	170
171	172	173	174	175	176	177	178	179	180
181	182	183	184	185	186	187	188	189	190
191	192	193	194	195	196	197	198	199	200

LEARN

201	202	203	204	205	206	207	208	209	210
211	212	213	214	215	216	217	218	219	220
221	222	223	224	225					
251	252	253	254	255	256	257	258	259	260
261	262	263	264	265	266	267	268	269	270
271	272	273	274	275	276	277	278	279	280
281	282	283	284	285	286	287	288	289	290
291	292	293	294	295	296	297	298	299	300

301	302	303	304	305	306	307	308	309	310
311	312	313	314	315	316	317	318	319	320
321	322	323	324	325	326	327	328	329	330
331	332	333	334	335	336	337	338	339	340
341	342	343	344	345	346	347	348	349	350
					376	377	378	379	380
381	382	383	384	385	386	387	388	389	390
391	392	393	394	395	396	397	398	399	400

L E A R N

Hundred Chart 4

401	402	403	404	405	406	407	408	409	410
411	412	413	414	415	416	417	418	419	420
421	422	423	424	425	426	427	428	429	430
431	432	433	434	435	436	437	438	439	440
441	442	443	444	445	446	447	448	449	450
451	452	453	454	455	456	457	458	459	460
461	462	463	464	465	466	467	468	469	470
471	472	473	474	475					

Write Numerals Through 500

Writing Numerals Through 500

Write the numbers as you hear them.

1. _____

2. _____

3. _____

4. _____

5. _____

6. Fill in the missing numbers in the partial hundred charts.

431	432		434	435	436	437		439	440

	202	203			206	207	208	209	

391	392	393	394	395	396		398		

		273	274	275	276	277	278	279	

TRY IT

Complete Problems 7–12.

7. Write the number for two hundred sixty-two. _____

8. Write the numbers for one hundred twenty-nine through one hundred thirty-nine.

   _____, _____, _____, _____, _____, _____,

   _____, _____, _____, _____, _____

9. Write the number for three hundred sixty-six. _____

10. Write the number for four hundred. _____

11. Write the number for three hundred three. _____

12. Write the numbers for four hundred fifty-five through four hundred sixty-five.

   _____, _____, _____, _____, _____, _____,

   _____, _____, _____, _____, _____

Identify Place Value
Place Value

Write the number shown in the place-value chart.

1.

Hundreds	Tens	Ones

_____

2.

Hundreds	Tens	Ones

_____

Write the value of each number given.

3. 5 in 256

_____

4. 6 in 256

_____

11

TRY IT

Write the value of each number given.

5. 4 in 437

_____

6. 3 in 437

_____

Circle the value for the underlined number.

7. 3<u>2</u>9

A. 2

B. 20

C. 200

8. 47<u>5</u>

A. 5

B. 50

C. 500

9. 19<u>8</u>

A. 8 ones

B. 8 tens

C. 8 hundreds

10. <u>2</u>41

A. 2 ones

B. 2 tens

C. 2 hundreds

11. <u>4</u>61

A. 4

B. 40

C. 400

12. 3<u>6</u>7

A. 6 ones

B. 6 tens

C. 6 hundreds

Complete the place value for each problem.

13. 409

_____ hundreds   _____ tens   _____ ones

14. 330

_____ hundreds   _____ tens   _____ ones

15. 160

_____ hundreds   _____ tens   _____ ones

16. 202

_____ hundreds   _____ tens   _____ ones

TRY IT

Use Expanded Form: Numbers Through 500

Expand a Number

Write each number in expanded form.

1. 345 = _____ hundreds + _____ tens + _____ ones

2. 204 = _____ hundreds + _____ tens + _____ ones

3. 460 = _____ hundreds + _____ tens + _____ ones

4. 369 = _____ + _____ + _____

5. 273 = _____ + _____ + _____

Write each number in standard form.

6. 2 hundreds + 8 tens + 7 ones = _____

7. 3 hundreds + 3 tens + 0 ones = _____

8. 200 + 60 + 6 = _____

9. 300 + 20 + 4 = _____

TRY IT

Choose the expanded form of each number.

10. 485

    A. 4 hundreds + 80 tens + 5 ones

    B. 40 hundreds + 8 tens + 5 ones

    C. 4 hundreds + 8 tens + 5 ones

    D. 48 hundreds + 5 ones

11. 77

    A. 7 + 7

    B. 7 + 0 + 7

    C. 70 + 70

    D. 70 + 7

Write the answer.

12. What is 299 written in expanded form?

_____ hundreds + _____ tens + _____ ones

Circle the answer.

13. Which of the following shows 453 in expanded form?

    A. 4 + 5 + 3

    B. 45 + 3

    C. 400 + 50 + 3

    D. 450 + 50 + 30

14. Which of the following shows 340 in expanded form?

    A. 34 + 0

    B. 3 + 4 + 0

    C. 3 + 40 + 0

    D. 300 + 40 + 0

TRY IT

Model Addition Problems

Model and Solve

Use base-10 blocks to show the numbers and find the sum for each problem.

1.
```
    T O
    37
 +  12
    49
```

2.
```
    45
 +  34
     9
```

3.
```
    68
 +  19
```

4.
```
    54
 +  27
```

5.
```
    211
 +  157
```

6.
```
    340
 +  236
```

7.
```
    246
 +  125
```

8.
```
    414
 +  349
```

TRY IT

Use base-10 blocks to show the numbers and find the sum for each problem.

9.
```
   29
+  12
_____
```

10.
```
   19
+  29
_____
```

11.
```
   79
+  36
_____
```

12.
```
  207
+  39
_____
```

13.
```
  127
+ 127
_____
```

14.
```
  346
+ 134
_____
```

15.
```
  119
+ 222
_____
```

16.
```
  255
+ 176
_____
```

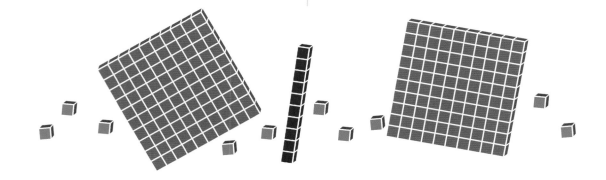

Place Value and Regrouping

Regrouping and Expanded Form

Write each number in expanded form.

1.

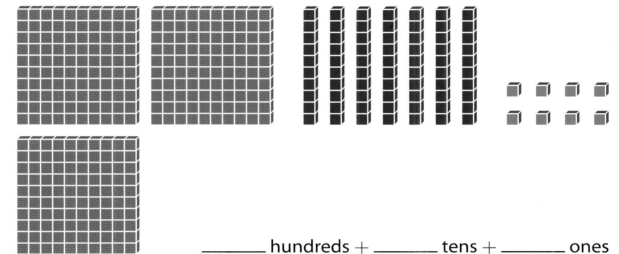

_____ hundreds + _____ tens + _____ ones

2.

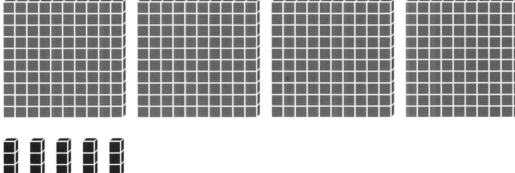

_____ hundreds + _____ tens + _____ ones

3. Write in standard form: 3 hundreds | 2 tens | 2 ones.

_____

T R Y   I T

4. Explain the value of the digits in the tens and ones places in Problem 3.

_____

_____

Model the numbers with base-10 blocks.
Then regroup and add. Write the sum on the line.

5. The sum of 236 and 147 is _____.

Circle the answer.

6. What is the value of the 9 in 389?

    A. 90   B. 9

    C. 19   D. 900

7. What is the value of the 4 in 243?

    A. 4 ones   B. 4 tens

    C. 4 hundreds   D. 40 tens

8. Draw base-10 blocks to model and solve this problem.

    The sum of 255 and 177 is _____.

9. Choose the expanded form of the following number: 485.

    A. 4 hundreds + 80 tens + 5 ones

    B. 40 hundreds + 8 tens + 5 ones

    C. 4 hundreds + 8 tens + 5 ones

    D. 48 hundreds + 5 ones

TRY IT

Compare Numbers Through 500

Compare Numbers

Compare the base-10 blocks. Write <, >, or = on the line.

1.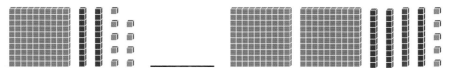

2.

3.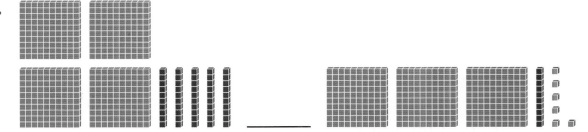

Compare the numbers. Write <, >, or = on the line.

4. 178 _____ 178

5. 298 _____ 276

6. 500 _____ 350

T R Y   I T

Compare the numbers. Choose <, >, or =.

7. 437 _____ 416

   A. <   B. >   C. =

8. 207 _____ 270

   A. <   B. >   C. =

9. 201 _____ 151

   A. <   B. >   C. =

10. 228 _____ 406

   A. <   B. >   C. =

11. Which number sentence is true?

   A. 466 > 366

   B. 248 < 159

   C. 385 > 494

   D. 264 < 246

12. Which number sentence is true?

   A. 166 > 66

   B. 458 < 358

   C. 185 > 285

   D. 267 < 167

Compare the numbers. Write the symbol that belongs on the line.

13. 333 _____ 222

14. 444 _____ 444

TRY IT

Comparing and Ordering
Put the Numbers in Order

Compare. Write $<$, $>$, or $=$ on the line.

1.

H	T	O
3	5	6
3	4	9

356 _____ 349

2.

H	T	O
4	0	8
4	0	8

408 _____ 408

3.

H	T	O
4	7	4
5	0	0

474 _____ 500

4.

H	T	O
2	6	4
2	4	6

264 _____ 246

5. 212 _____ 221

6. 350 _____ 350

7. 178 _____ 198 _____ 213

8. 344 _____ 344 _____ 334

9. 259 _____ 399 _____ 450

T R Y   I T

Compare. Choose <, >, or =.

10. 323 _____ 323

    A.   <   B.   >   C.   =

11. 208 _____ 280

    A.   <   B.   >   C.   =

Which number goes on the line?

12. 58 > _____ > 45

    A.   65   B.   52   C.   45   D.   36

13. 251 > _____ > 201

    A.   231   B.   251   C.   262   D.   299

Compare. Write <, >, or =.

14. 98 _____ 98 _____ 100

15. 349 _____ 241 _____ 196

TRY IT

Order Whole Numbers Through 500

Order These Numbers

Circle the number that makes the number sentence true.

1. $199 <$ _____   195   209   189

2. _____ < 350 396   423   317

3. $172 >$ _____   167   271   175

4. _____ > 350 310   318   431

5. $342 =$ _____   243   342   493

Order each set of numbers. Write the numbers on the lines.

6. least to greatest
218, 313, 256   _____ $<$ _____ $<$ _____

7. greatest to least
249, 464, 325   _____ $>$ _____ $>$ _____

8. least to greatest
500, 491, 416   _____ $<$ _____ $<$ _____

TRY IT

Circle the answer.

9. Which number sentence is true?

    A. $488 = 489$

    B. $322 = 322$

    C. $499 = 489$

    D. $355 = 255$

10. Which number sentence is true?

    A. $289 < 279$

    B. $109 > 110$

    C. $329 > 319$

    D. $488 = 487$

11. Which number goes on the line?

    $67 < \text{_____} < 87$

    A. 65

    B. 77

    C. 89

    D. 97

12. Which number sentence is true?

    A. $434 < 457 < 489$

    B. $419 < 409 < 427$

    C. $481 < 475 < 465$

    D. $499 < 457 < 436$

13. Which number sentence is true?

    A. $243 < 251 < 236$

    B. $275 < 269 < 241$

    C. $275 < 286 < 293$

    D. $229 < 215 < 251$

14. Write the number that would make the number sentence true.

    $316 < \text{_____} < 318$

TRY IT

Read Number Words Through 500

Number Words

Write a number for each number word.

1. eighty

_____

2. one hundred eleven

_____

3. nineteen

_____

4. four hundred fifty-one

_____

5. two hundred seventeen

_____

6. ninety-nine

_____

7. three hundred seventy-six

_____

8. two hundred eight

_____

9. forty-three

_____

10. four hundred eighty

_____

11. sixteen

_____

12. fifty-two

_____

T R Y   I T

13. Write the number 200 in word form.

_____

14. Write the number 400 in word form.

_____

15. Write the number 233 in word form.

_____

16. Write the number 155 in word form.

_____

17. Write the number 309 in word form.

_____

18. Write the number 104 in word form.

_____

19. Write the number 168 in word form.

_____

20. Write the number 446 in word form.

_____

TRY IT

Unit Review

Checkpoint Practice

Fill in the missing numbers.

1. 361, 362, _____, 364, 365, _____, 367, 368, 369, _____

2. _____, 192, 193, _____, 195, 196, _____, 198, 199, 200

3. Circle the greatest number.   24   214   145

4. Circle the least number.   376   318   352

5. Write the numbers in order from least to greatest.

   217   189   108   213   _____ _____ _____ _____

Write the number in expanded form.

6. 419 _____

7. 186 _____

Write the number for each number word.

8. twenty-seven _____

9. two hundred ninety-four _____

Circle the answer.

10. What is the value of the 4 in 243?

    A. 4 ones   B. 4 tens

    C. 4 hundreds   D. 40 tens

11. Which digit is in the hundreds place?   654

    A. 6   B. 5   C. 4

12. Choose the expanded form of the following number: 476.

    A. 40 hundreds + 76 ones   B. 4 hundreds + 6 tens + 7 ones

    C. 4 hundreds + 7 tens + 6 ones   D. 47 hundreds + 0 tens + 6 ones

13. Which number sentence is true?

    A. 185 < 164 < 159   B. 135 > 196 > 171

    C. 123 < 134 < 155   D. 162 > 177 > 148

14. Which of the following shows the number 33 in word form?

    A. thirty-three   B. 3 + 3

    C. three three   D. three hundred three

15. Compare. Choose <, >, or =.   437 ___ 416

    A. <   B. >   C. =

Write the answer.

16. Write the number 401 in word form. _____

17. Write the number for four hundred fifty-one. _____

18. Compare. Write the symbol that belongs on the line.   171 _____ 160

UNIT REVIEW

Time to the Nearest Quarter Hour

A Quarter After the Hour

Draw the hour and minute hands on the clock to show the time.
Write the time below the clock.

1.

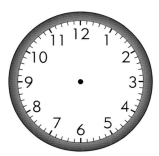

_____ : _____

2.

_____ : _____

3.

_____ : _____

4.

_____ : _____

5.

_____ : _____

6.

_____ : _____

L E A R N

A Quarter 'til the Hour

Draw the hour and minute hands on the clock to show the time.
Write the time below the clock.

1.

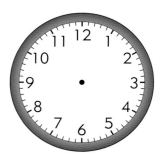

____ : ____

2.

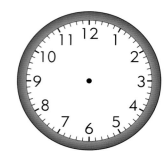

____ : ____

3.

____ : ____

4.

____ : ____

5.

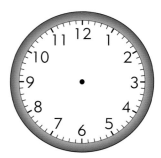

____ : ____

6.

____ : ____

LEARN

Time to the Nearest Quarter Hour

Time Will Tell

Write the time shown on the clock to the nearest quarter hour.

1.

_____ : _____

2.

_____ : _____

3.

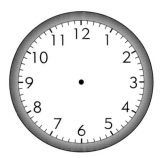

_____ : _____

4.

_____ : _____

Draw hands on the clock to show the time.

5. 4 : 45

6. 12 : 45

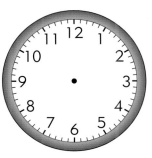

7. 6 : 15

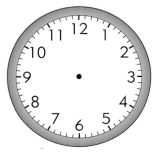

8. 2 : 30

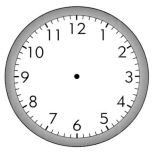

T R Y   I T

Circle the answer.

9. What time does the clock show?

A. 12:15

B. 1:15

C. 9:45

D. 2:15

10. What time does the clock show?

A. 7:45

B. 6:45

C. 8:15

D. 5:15

11. About what time does the clock show?

A. 3:15

B. 9:45

C. 10:45

D. 11:15

12. About what time does the clock show?

A. 3:15

B. 9:15

C. 10:45

D. 5:45

Draw hands on the clock to show the time.

13. 3:15

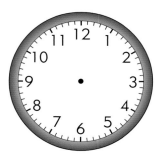

14. 11:45

15. 4:45

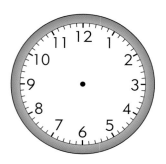

16. 10:15

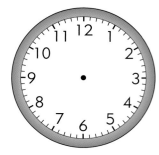

TRY IT

Time Relationships
Equivalent Times

Draw lines to match the amounts of time on one side with the amounts of time on the other side.

7 days •   • 1 year

60 minutes •   • 1 day

1 minute •   • 1 week

24 hours •   • 1 hour

1 year •   • 60 seconds

12 months •   • 52 weeks

TRY IT

Circle the answer.

1. How many hours are in one day?
   A. 12
   B. 20
   C. 24
   D. 30

2. How many seconds are in one minute?
   A. 50
   B. 60
   C. 70
   D. 100

3. How many minutes are in one hour?
   A. 12
   B. 24
   C. 60
   D. 100

4. How many months are in one year?
   A. 10
   B. 12
   C. 15
   D. 20

5. How many days are in one week?
   A. 5
   B. 6
   C. 7
   D. 8

6. How many weeks are in one year?
   A. 7
   B. 14
   C. 30
   D. 52

7. Lisa went to summer camp for two weeks. How many days was she at camp?
   A. 10
   B. 12
   C. 14
   D. 7

8. How many weeks are in two years?
   A. 7
   B. 24
   C. 52
   D. 104

TRY IT

Elapsed Time

Show Elapsed Time

Draw the hour and minute hands on the END clock to show the elapsed time.

1.

BEGIN   END

elapsed time = 4 hours

2.

BEGIN   END

elapsed time = 8 hours

Write the number of hours that have elapsed.

3. 5:00 a.m. to 8:00 a.m.

_____

4. 1:00 p.m. to 7:00 p.m.

_____

5. 9:00 a.m. to 2:00 p.m.

_____

6. 7:00 p.m. to 4:00 a.m.

_____

TRY IT

Circle the answer.

7. How many hours are there from 12:00 noon to 5:00 p.m.?

   A. 5   B. 6   C. 7   D. 8

8. How many hours are there from 8:00 a.m. to 11:00 a.m.?

   A. 1   B. 2   C. 3   D. 4

9. How many hours are there from 10:00 a.m. to 5:00 p.m.?

   A. 5   B. 6   C. 7   D. 8

10. How many hours are there from 7:00 p.m. to 1:00 a.m.?

    A. 3   B. 4   C. 5   D. 6

11. Sam has to be at practice at 10:00 a.m. It is 7:00 a.m. now. How many hours are there until Sam has to be at practice?

    A. 2   B. 3

    C. 8   D. 12

12. Isabelle's clay was put on a shelf to dry at 2:00 p.m. and was dry at 10:00 p.m. How many hours did the clay take to dry?

    A. 8   B. 9

    C. 10   D. 11

TRY IT

Find the Value of Coins or Bills

How Much?

Count to find the value for the groups of coins and bills.
Say each amount aloud.

1.

2.

3.

4.

Write the amount shown in each group of coins or bills.

5. How many cents are shown below?

_____

6. How many cents are shown below?

_____

7. What is the value of this group of coins?

_____

8. How many dollars are shown below?

_____

9. How many dollars are shown below?

_____

Dollar and Cent Symbols for Money

Cent Symbol

Use the cent symbol to write each amount.

1. 20 cents = _____

2. 1 cent = _____

3. 75 cents = _____

4.    = _____

5.   = _____

Fill in the blank.

6. The cent symbol always goes _____ the number of cents.

LEARN

Dollar Symbol

Use the dollar symbol to write each dollar amount.

1.   = _____

2. 6 dollars = _____

3. 15 dollars = _____

4. 21 dollars = _____

5.  = _____

6.    = _____

Fill in the blank.

7. The dollar symbol always goes _____ the dollar amount.

Dollar and Cent Symbols for Money

Write Money Amounts Using Symbols

Use the cent symbol or dollar symbol to write the value of the coins or bills shown.

1.

_____

2.

_____

3.

_____

4.

_____

5.

_____

TRY IT

Use the cent symbol to write the value of the coins.

6.   _____

Fill in the blanks.

7. The dollar symbol always goes _____ the amount of money,

and the cent symbol always goes _____ the amount of money.

Circle the answer.

8. Which one of the following symbols stands for cents?
   A. %   B. $ C. ¢   D. #

9. Which one of the following symbols stands for dollars?
   A. %   B. $ C. ¢   D. #

10. Choose the correct way to write 100¢.
   A. $100   B. $10   C. $.01   D. $1

11. Choose the correct way to write thirteen dollars.
   A. 13$ B. $130   C. $13   D. $130

12. Choose the correct way to write the value of the coins shown.

   A. 28¢   B. $028   C. ¢28   D. 280$

TRY IT

Decimal Notation for Money

Money as Dollars and Cents

Find the value of each group of money. Then write each amount, using a dollar symbol and a decimal point.

1.

_____

2.

_____

Listen carefully to the amount of money read to you.
Use decimal notation to write the amount.

3. _____   **4.** _____

5. _____   **6.** _____

TRY IT

Circle the answer.

7. What is another way to write 1 penny?

   A. $1   B. $0.1   C. $0.01   D. $10

8. What is another way to write 13 cents?

   A. $13   B. $1.3   C. $0.13   D. $130

9. What is another way to write 10 cents?

   A. $1   B. $0.10   C. $0.01   D. $10

10. What is another way to write 25 cents?

   A. $2.5   B. $0.25   C. $0.025   D. $25

---

11. Write two dollars and fifty-one cents using decimal notation.

   _____

12. Write eleven dollars and ninety-nine cents using decimal notation.

   _____

13. Write seventeen dollars and seventeen cents using decimal notation.

   _____

14. Write twenty dollars and two cents using decimal notation.

   _____

T R Y   I T

Fewest Bills and Coins

You're in the Money

Look at the money you are given. Trade to show the fewest bills and coins that make the same value.

1. $0.52

2. $9.00

3. $17.29

Look at the amount shown. Use your money to show the fewest bills and coins that make that amount.

4. $6.08

5. $24.67

Circle the answer.

6. Which answer shows a different way to show this much money?

A.

B.

C.

D.

TRY IT

7. Which answer shows a different way to show this much money?

A.

B.

C.

D.

Look at the amount shown. Use your money to show the fewest bills and coins that make that amount.

8. $0.88

9. $23.65

TRY IT

How Much Money?

Solve Money Problems

Name:

Circle the exact amount needed to buy the item.

1. A skateboard costs $17.55.

Circle Yes or No.

2. Milk costs $3.79. Do you have enough money to buy milk?   Yes   No

47

T R Y I T

Count the amount. Write the total.

3. Yuri received 3 dollar bills, 6 quarters, and 12 dimes.

   How much money did she get in all? _____

4. Verna sells lemonade. Today she collected 4 dollar bills, 9 quarters, 11 dimes, and 6 nickels.

   How much money did she collect in all? _____

Count the bills and coins. Write the total.

5.

_____

TRY IT

Circle the answer.

6. Jayden has 1 dollar bill, 1 quarter, and 2 pennies. How much money does he have?

   A. $1.26   B. $1.27

   C. $1.28   D. $1.29

7. Mia has the money you see below. How much money does she have?

   A. $2.10   B. $5.10

   C. $5.11   D. $6.10

8. Pedro has $1.25. Which answer choice shows how much money Pedro has?

A.

B.

C.

D.

Circle the answer.

9. Sherry needs $3.75 to buy a new ball at the sports shop. Choose the amount of money that Sherry needs.

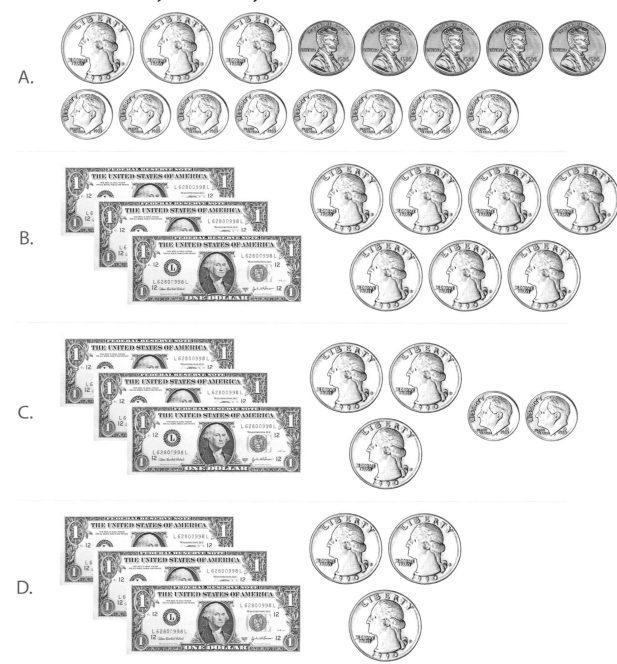

A.

B.

C.

D.

___

Write the total.

10. Simon and Anna have been saving for a new movie. Together they have saved 7 dollar bills, 6 quarters, and 8 dimes.

How much money have they saved in all? _____

Unit Review

Checkpoint Practice

Write the time to the nearest quarter hour.

1.

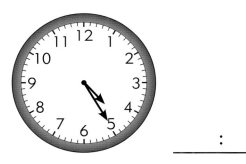

_____ : _____

2.

_____ : _____

Fill in the correct number.

3. There are _____ minutes in 1 hour.

4. There are _____ hours in 1 day.

Write the number of hours that have passed between these times.

5. 6:00 a.m. to 11:00 a.m.

_____

Use the dollar symbol or the cent symbol to write the value of the bills and coins shown.

6.

_____

Write which bills and coins are needed to make the amount shown.
Use the fewest number of bills and coins.

7. $9.32 _____

_____

Circle the answer.

8. Choose the correct way to write one dollar and seventy-six cents.

   A. ¢176   B. $1.76   C. $176   D. $17.60

9. Carlos has 1 dollar bill, 2 quarters, and 3 nickels. How much money does he have?

   A. $1.65

   B. $1.66

   C. $1.67

   D. $1.68

10. Jenny has the money you see below. How much money does she have?

   A. $5.21

   B. $5.22

   C. $5.23

   D. $5.24

11. Which answer shows a different way to show this much money?

A.    B.

C.    D.

Addition and Subtraction

Model Addition and Subtraction

Use base-10 blocks to show the addition and subtraction problems.
Write the sum or difference on the line.

1. 235 + 187 = _____

2. 327 − 192 = _____

3. 426 − 304 = _____

4. 195 + 238 = _____

5. 304 − 157 = _____

6. 299 + 166 = _____

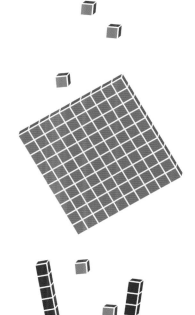
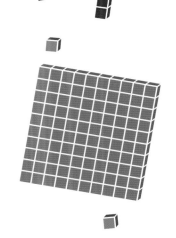

TRY IT

Use base-10 blocks and a place-value mat to solve the problems on this page. For Problems 7 and 8, circle the answer.

7. $178 + 281$

    A. 359   B. 259   C. 117   D. 459

8. $450 - 388$

    A. 838   B. 162   C. 62   D. 238

9. Solve. Write the answer on the line. $123 + 298 =$ _____

10. Draw a model you could use to help you solve this subtraction problem.

$$\begin{array}{r} 38 \\ -\ 20 \\ \hline \end{array}$$

11. Use base-10 blocks to model and solve this problem.

$$\begin{array}{r} 481 \\ -\ 24 \\ \hline \end{array}$$

TRY IT

Addition Computation Through 500

Modeling Addition

For Problem 1, use base-10 blocks and a place-value mat to find the sum.
For Problems 2 and 3, use only the place-value charts to find the sums.

Example

179
+ 115

	H	T	O
		1	
	1	7	9
+	1	1	5
	2	9	4

1. 317
+ 98

	H	T	O
+			

2. 256
+ 178

	H	T	O
+			

3. 256
+ 241

	H	T	O
+			

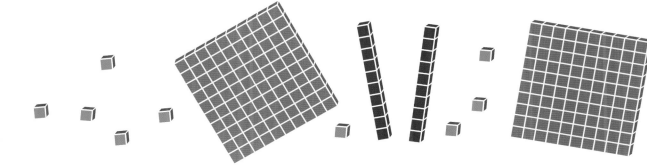

LEARN

Addition with Regrouping

Find the sums. First write the numbers in the place-value chart, and then add the numbers.

1. $329 + 89 =$ _____

	H	T	O
$+$			

2. $315 + 164 =$ _____

	H	T	O
$+$			

3. $138 + 148 =$ _____

	H	T	O
$+$			

4. $275 + 149 =$ _____

	H	T	O
$+$			

LEARN

Addition Computation Through 500

Addition Computation

Use the place-value chart to find the sum.

1.   140
      + 53

	H	T	O
+			

Circle any place values that needed regrouping.

hundreds   tens   ones

2.   224
      + 181

	H	T	O
+			

Circle any place values that needed regrouping.

hundreds   tens   ones

3.   128 + 126 = _____

	H	T	O
+			

Circle any place values that needed regrouping.

hundreds   tens   ones

4.   285 + 147 = _____

	H	T	O
+			

Circle any place values that needed regrouping.

hundreds   tens   ones

TRY IT

Solve Problems 5–7 by adding. You may use the Place-Value Chart
(Hundreds) to solve.

5.   97
        $+\ 33$

6.   345
        $+\ 56$

7.   196
        $+\ 34$

Circle the answer.

8. $391 + 34 =$ _____

   A. 357   B. 325   C. 425   D. 415

TRY IT

Finding the Difference

Regroup and Subtract

Use the place-value chart to find the difference. Circle any place values that needed regrouping.

1. 91
  − 68

H	T	O
─		

Circle any place values that needed regrouping.

hundreds   tens   ones

2. 474
  − 355

H	T	O
─		

Circle any place values that needed regrouping.

hundreds   tens   ones

3. 266
  − 198

H	T	O
─		

Circle any place values that needed regrouping.

hundreds   tens   ones

4. 302
  − 260

H	T	O
─		

Circle any place values that needed regrouping.

hundreds   tens   ones

TRY IT

Solve.

5.   235
    − 66
    _____

Circle the answer.

6.   496
    − 37
    _____

   A. 381   B. 459
   C. 421   D. 375

7.   385
    − 126
    _____

   A. 227   B. 238
   C. 259   D. 271

TRY IT

Subtraction and the Equals Symbol

Equals Symbol with Subtraction

Find the difference for each subtraction problem.

1.
$$\begin{array}{r} 466 \\ -\ 75 \\ \hline \end{array}$$

2.
$$\begin{array}{r} 350 \\ -\ 175 \\ \hline \end{array}$$

3.
$$\begin{array}{r} 297 \\ -\ 95 \\ \hline \end{array}$$

4.
$$\begin{array}{r} 445 \\ -\ 265 \\ \hline \end{array}$$

Circle the answer.

5.
$$\begin{array}{r} 437 \\ -\ 256 \\ \hline \end{array}$$

   A. 181   B. 231

   C. 243   D. 193

6.
$$\begin{array}{r} 430 \\ -\ 287 \\ \hline \end{array}$$

   A. 143   B. 137

   C. 128   D. 111

7.
$$\begin{array}{r} 500 \\ -\ 75 \\ \hline \end{array}$$

   A. 375   B. 425

   C. 395   D. 455

TRY IT

Decide whether the two amounts are equal.
Write an equals symbol in the box if they are equal.

8. $14 - 6$ ☐ 8

9. $20 - 11$ ☐ 10

10. 7 ☐ $15 - 8$

11. $22 - 9$ ☐ 13

Read the problem and follow the directions.

12. What does the equals symbol mean in this number sentence?

$$8 = 4 + 4$$

_____

_____

13. What does the symbol the arrow is pointing to mean? Circle the answer.

$$34 + 2 \stackrel{\downarrow}{=} 36 + 0$$

A. is the same as

B. find the answer

C. add all the numbers together

D. subtract the small number from the larger one

14. Which symbol belongs in the box? Circle the answer.

$$8 + 4 \ \boxed{} \ 12$$

A. $+$ C. $<$ B. $-$ D. $=$

Decompose Numbers

Break Numbers

Complete each fact family triangle to show the number.

1.

13

− −

+

_____   7

2.

130

− −

+

60   _____

3.

60

− −

+

30   _____

4.

67

− −

+

30   _____

5.

22

− −

+

_____   12

6.

220

− −

+

10   _____

7.

25

− −

+

20   _____

8.

256

− −

+

200   _____

T R Y   I T

Circle the answer.

9. What is another way to write eighty-five?

    A. $40 + 45$ B. $8 + 5$

    C. $80 + 50$ D. $8 + 50$

---

10. What is another way to write $40 + 50$?

    A. 450   B. 4,050

    C. 90   D. 900

Complete the number sentences by filling in the blank.

11. $28 = 20 +$ _____

12. $280 = 200 +$ _____

13. $42 = 20 +$ _____

14. $420 = 200 +$ _____

TRY IT

Make and Break Numbers

Model Numbers in Expanded Form

Name: _____

Model and write each number two different ways. One of the ways should be in expanded form.

1. 184 = _____   _____

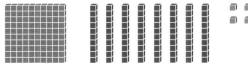

2. 319 = _____   _____

3. 491 = _____   _____

Write each number two different ways.

4. 257

_____   _____

5. 208

_____   _____

6. 447

_____   _____

L E A R N

Circle the answer.

7. Which model shows the number 348?

A.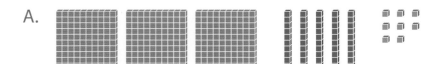

B.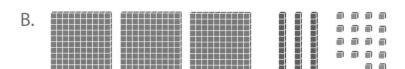

C.

D.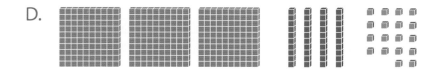

Make and Break Numbers

Use Expanded Form

Write each number in expanded form.

1. 283 = _____

2. 499 = _____

3. 132 = _____

4. 326 = _____

Write each expanded notation another way.

5. 219 = 200 + 10 + 9 _____

6. 162 = 100 + 60 + 2 _____

Circle Yes or No. Write the numbers in expanded notation.

7. Katie has 2 hundreds flats and 18 ones cubes. Ryan has 2 hundreds flats, 1 tens rod, and 8 ones cubes. Do they have the same number?

A. Yes

B. No

_____

8. Calvin has 3 hundreds flats, 6 tens rods, and 4 ones cubes. Anna has 3 hundreds flats, 4 tens rods, and 14 ones cubes. Do they have the same number?

A. Yes

B. No

_____

TRY IT

67

Circle the answer.

9. What is another way to write $300 + 30 + 4$?

    A. 330   B. 334   C. 433   D. 300

Write the answer to each question.

10. What is another way to write 323?

_____

11. What is another way to write 122?

_____

12. Tony has 2 hundreds flats and 14 ones cubes. David has 1 hundreds flat, 11 tens rods, and 4 ones cubes. Do their blocks model the same number? Write two number sentences to show your thinking.

_____

TRY IT

Break Up Numbers

Break Up Numbers

Circle the answer.

1. What is another way to write one hundred thirty-six?

    A. $100 + 3 + 6$ B. $1 + 3 + 6$

    C. $100 + 30 + 6$ D. $1 + 30 + 6$

2. Which of the following is another way to write 499?

    A. $400 + 9 + 9$ B. $4 + 9 + 9$

    C. $400 + 90 + 9$ D. $490 + 99$

3. Which of the following is another way to write 100?

    A. $50 + 50$ B. $40 + 40 + 40$

    C. $50 + 100$ D. $100 + 100$

4. Which of the following is another way to write 76?

    A. $7 + 6$ B. $70 + 6$

    C. $76 + 6$ D. $76 - 6$

5. You can write 126 as $100 + 20 + 6$. What is another way to write 126?

    A. $1 + 2 + 6$ B. $100 + 16 + 10$

    C. $100 - 16 - 10$ D. $100 + 26 + 1$

TRY IT

Use the open number line to show how you break apart the numbers to add.

6. $51 + 49 =$ _____

7. $99 + 101 =$ _____

8. $125 + 150 =$ _____

9. $230 + 175 =$ _____

TRY IT

Breaking Numbers to Subtract

Break Numbers Using Number Lines

Find the difference by using the number lines to break apart the numbers.

1.   117 – 9 = _____

2.   342 – 18 = _____

3.   284 – 25 = _____

4.   428 – 12 = _____

TRY IT

5. $165 - 29 =$ _____

6. $353 - 7 =$ _____

7. $220 - 19 =$ _____

8. $356 - 52 =$ _____

9. $245 - 17 =$ _____

10. $78 - 13 =$ _____

TRY IT

Decompose to Subtract

Subtract by Breaking Numbers

Find the difference by breaking one or both of the numbers apart. Show your work on the number line.

1. $245 - 18 =$ _____

2. $461 - 23 =$ _____

3. $274 - 39 =$ _____

4. $192 - 15 =$ _____

L E A R N

Write Number Sentences

Break apart numbers to solve the subtraction problems. Show your work on the number lines. Then write number sentences to tell what you did.

1. $365 - 48 =$ _____

_____

2. $91 - 58 =$ _____

_____

3. $146 - 56 =$ _____

_____

4. $486 - 446 =$ _____

_____

Decompose to Subtract

Break Apart Numbers to Subtract

Break apart numbers to find each difference.

1. $81 - 17 =$ _____

⟵──────────────────────────────⟶

2. $147 - 9 =$ _____

⟵──────────────────────────────⟶

3. $352 - 27 =$ _____

⟵──────────────────────────────⟶

4. $445 - 16 =$ _____

⟵──────────────────────────────⟶

TRY IT

5. $93 - 25 = $ _____

6. $130 - 14 = $ _____

Choose the number sentence that can be used to solve each problem.

7. $47 - 28 = $ _____

    A. $47 + 26 + 26$

    B. $47 - 27 - 1$

    C. $20 + 27 + 26$

    D. $47 + 26 + 27$

8. $510 - 11 = $ _____

    A. $510 - 10 - 1$

    B. $500 - 11$

    C. $510 + 10 - 11$

    D. $500 - 10 - 1$

Write a number sentence that could help you solve each problem, and then solve each problem.

9. $108 - 14 = $ _____

_____ $= $ _____

10. $209 - 16 = $ _____

_____ $= $ _____

TRY IT

Unit Review

Checkpoint Practice

Find the sum or difference. You may use your
base-10 blocks and place-value mat to help you.

1. $308 + 119 =$ _____

2. $352 - 161 =$ _____

Find each sum or difference. You may use your base-10 blocks and
place-value mat to help you.

3.
$$\begin{array}{r} 87 \\ -\ 23 \\ \hline \end{array}$$

4.
$$\begin{array}{r} 237 \\ +\ 88 \\ \hline \end{array}$$

5.
$$\begin{array}{r} 103 \\ -\ 67 \\ \hline \end{array}$$

6.
$$\begin{array}{r} 278 \\ +\ 104 \\ \hline \end{array}$$

7.
$$\begin{array}{r} 247 \\ +\ 199 \\ \hline \end{array}$$

8.
$$\begin{array}{r} 263 \\ -\ 135 \\ \hline \end{array}$$

Break apart the numbers to make them easier to add or subtract. Then find each sum or difference. Show your work.

9. $160 - 45 =$ _____

10. $145 + 220 =$ _____

11. $300 + 125 =$ _____

12. $471 - 67 =$ _____

Decide whether the two amounts are equal. Write $=$ in the box if the amounts are equal, and $\neq$ in the box if they are not equal.

13. $17 - 8 \;\boxed{}\; 8$

14. $16 + 12 \;\boxed{}\; 28$

15. $7 \;\boxed{}\; 19 - 7$

16. $16 \;\boxed{}\; 16 + 0$

UNIT REVIEW

17. What does the equals symbol mean in this number sentence?

$7 - 0 = 3 + 4$

_____

Which symbol belongs on the line?
Circle the answer.

18. 12 _____ $6 + 6$

    A. $\neq$

    B. $=$

    C. $-$

    D. $+$

19. $2 + 8$ _____ $10 - 0$

    A. $=$

    B. $\neq$

    C. $-$

    D. $+$

20. Which of the following is another way to write 91?

    A. $9 + 1$

    B. $90 - 1$

    C. $90 + 1$

    D. $99 + 9$

21. What is another way to write $200 + 40 + 8$?

    A. 248

    B. 842

    C. 428

    D. 284

22. Write a number sentence to show how you would break apart the numbers to make them easier to add or subtract.

$445 - 13 =$ _____

Which other number sentence can be used to solve the problem? Circle the answer.

23. $289 - 15 =$ _____

    A. $200 + 89 + 15$

    B. $270 + 19 - 15$

    C. $289 + 15$

    D. $279 + 15 + 19$

24. $456 - 13 =$ _____

    A. $56 + 13$

    B. $400 - 100$

    C. $456 + 56 + 13$

    D. $440 + 16 - 13$

Add.

25.
$$\begin{array}{r} 55 \\ + 79 \\ \hline \end{array}$$

26.
$$\begin{array}{r} 165 \\ + 78 \\ \hline \end{array}$$

27.
$$\begin{array}{r} 287 \\ + 63 \\ \hline \end{array}$$

Find the difference.

28.
$$\begin{array}{r} 482 \\ - 37 \\ \hline \end{array}$$

29.
$$\begin{array}{r} 239 \\ - 46 \\ \hline \end{array}$$

30.
$$\begin{array}{r} 387 \\ - 163 \\ \hline \end{array}$$

    A. 211 B. 224

    C. 237 D. 242

---

31. Use base-10 blocks to model and solve this problem.

$$\begin{array}{r} 121 \\ + 111 \\ \hline \end{array}$$

32. Use base-10 blocks to model and solve this problem.

$$\begin{array}{r} 382 \\ + 112 \\ \hline \end{array}$$

Opposite Operations: + and −

Show Opposite Operations

Write two addition number sentences for the fact triangle. Then write two related subtraction sentences. The first two are shown as an example.

1.

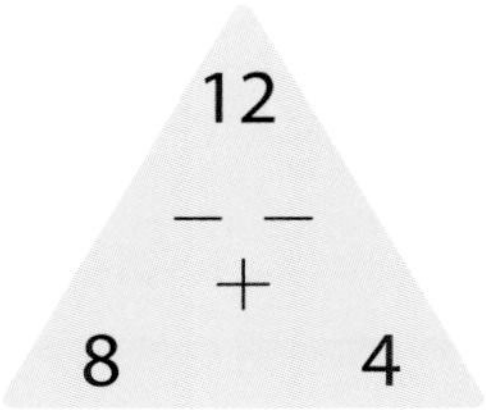

Triangle: 12 at top, − − / + , 8 and 4 at bottom

$8 + 4 = 12$ $12 - 8 = 4$

$\square + \square = \square$ $\square - \square = \square$

2.

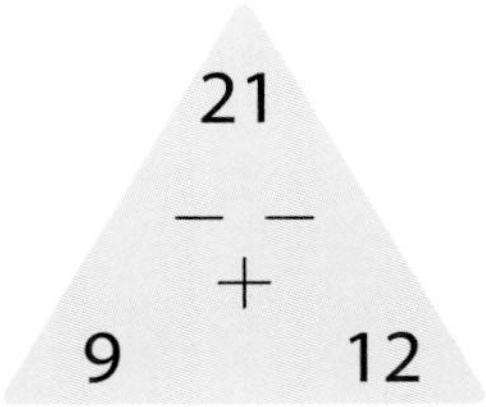

Triangle: 21 at top, − − / + , 9 and 12 at bottom

$\square + \square = \square$ $\square - \square = \square$

$\square + \square = \square$ $\square - \square = \square$

3.

Triangle: 25 at top, − − / + , 10 and 15 at bottom

$\square + \square = \square$ $\square - \square = \square$

$\square + \square = \square$ $\square - \square = \square$

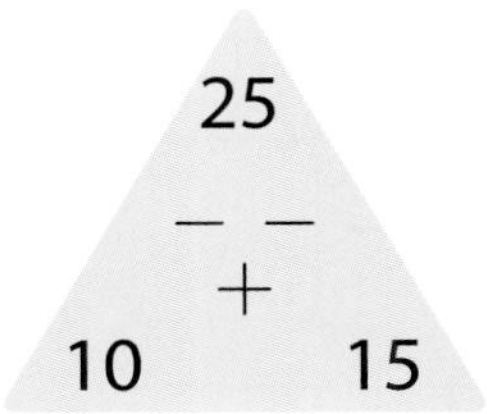

4. Look at the number sentence. Write the related addition facts.

$20 - 6 = 14$

$\square + \square = \square$

$\square + \square = \square$

5. Look at the number sentence. Write the related subtraction facts. Explain why you wrote the fact you did.

$300 + 100 = 400$

$\square - \square = \square$

$\square - \square = \square$

LEARN

How Are They Related?

Write the two addition facts that can be used to check.

Example: $14 - 5 = 9$

$$\boxed{5} + \boxed{9} = \boxed{14}$$

$$\boxed{9} + \boxed{5} = \boxed{14}$$

---

1. $22 - 10 = 12$

$$\boxed{} + \boxed{} = \boxed{}$$

$$\boxed{} + \boxed{} = \boxed{}$$

2. $30 - 10 = 20$

$$\boxed{} + \boxed{} = \boxed{}$$

$$\boxed{} + \boxed{} = \boxed{}$$

Write the related addition and subtraction facts.

3.

17

$-$ $-$
$+$

7   10

$$\boxed{} + \boxed{} = \boxed{} \qquad \boxed{} - \boxed{} = \boxed{}$$

$$\boxed{} + \boxed{} = \boxed{} \qquad \boxed{} - \boxed{} = \boxed{}$$

---

4. Serena did this subtraction problem. Write an addition sentence she can use to check her work. $23 - 8 = 15$

_____

Opposite Operations: + and −

Addition and Subtraction Are Opposites

1. How are addition and subtraction related?

   _____

2. Write a related addition fact to check $33 - 25 = 8$. Explain your answer.

   _____

3. Draw circles to show the sum of the parts shown. Use the chart to write the addition facts. Then write the related subtraction facts.

Whole _____	
9 Part	**6** Part

   $9 + \boxed{} = 15$

   $6 + \boxed{} = \boxed{}$

   $15 - \boxed{} = \boxed{}$

   $\boxed{} - \boxed{} = \boxed{}$

4. Draw circles to show the sum of the parts shown. Use the chart to write the addition facts. Then write the related subtraction facts.

Whole _____	
6 Part	**7** Part

   $6 + \boxed{} = \boxed{}$

   $7 + \boxed{} = \boxed{}$

   $\boxed{} - \boxed{} = \boxed{}$

   $\boxed{} - \boxed{} = \boxed{}$

TRY IT

Write a related subtraction sentence that you can use to check each problem.

5. $12 + 13 = 25$

6. $25 + 25 = 50$

Write a related addition sentence that you can use to check each problem.

7. $28 - 8 = 20$

8. $30 - 13 = 17$

Read the problem and follow the directions.

9. Molly has 10 apples and she is given 3 more. She adds them up and decides that she now has 13 apples. Draw a picture to show this addition sentence and then write a subtraction sentence to show how many apples Molly started with.

10. Dana did this subtraction problem $67 - 33 = 34$. Write an addition problem she can use to check her work.

11. Write a related addition fact for $15 - 6 = 9$.

12. Paul did this addition problem $2 + 6 = 8$. Which subtraction problem shows that he got the answer right? Circle the answer.

A. $8 + 6 = 14$

B. $8 + 2 = 10$

C. $8 - 6 = 2$

D. $10 - 8 = 6$

TRY IT

Mental Math: Addition and Subtraction

Find the Answer Mentally

Use mental math to find each sum.

1. $60 + 37 =$ _____

2. $71 + 18 =$ _____

3. $15 + 24 =$ _____

4. $94 + 13 =$ _____

5. $39 + 42 =$ _____

6. $55 + 27 =$ _____

Use mental math to find each difference.

7. $80 - 50 =$ _____

8. $65 - 12 =$ _____

9. $90 - 44 =$ _____

10. $77 - 20 =$ _____

11. $58 - 34 =$ _____

12. $46 - 19 =$ _____

TRY IT

Use mental math to find each sum or difference. Circle the answer.

13. $22 + 10 =$ _____

    A. 23   B. 32

    C. 33   D. 26

14. $47 + 12 =$ _____

    A. 35   B. 51

    C. 59   D. 62

15. $35 + 7 =$ _____

    A. 30   B. 32

    C. 40   D. 42

16. $54 + 55 =$ _____

    A. 59   B. 106

    C. 109   D. 119

17. $64 - 24 =$ _____

    A. 88   B. 52

    C. 40   D. 30

18. $35 - 22 =$ _____

    A. 13   B. 17

    C. 21   D. 23

19. $45 - 17 =$ _____

    A. 28   B. 35

    C. 38   D. 40

20. $120 - 19 =$ _____

    A. 80   B. 91

    C. 100   D. 101

TRY IT

Strategies to Add & Subtract Through 500

Use Addition Strategies

Solve each problem. You may use open number lines (below), place-value charts (on the back of this sheet), or a model to find the answer. Explain your steps.

1. $125 + 133 =$ _____

2. $114 + 239 =$ _____

3. $350 + 125 =$ _____

4. $125 + 158 =$ _____

5. $33 + 49 =$ _____

6. $45 + 33 =$ _____

7. $73 + 36 =$ _____

8. $58 + 67 =$ _____

T R Y   I T

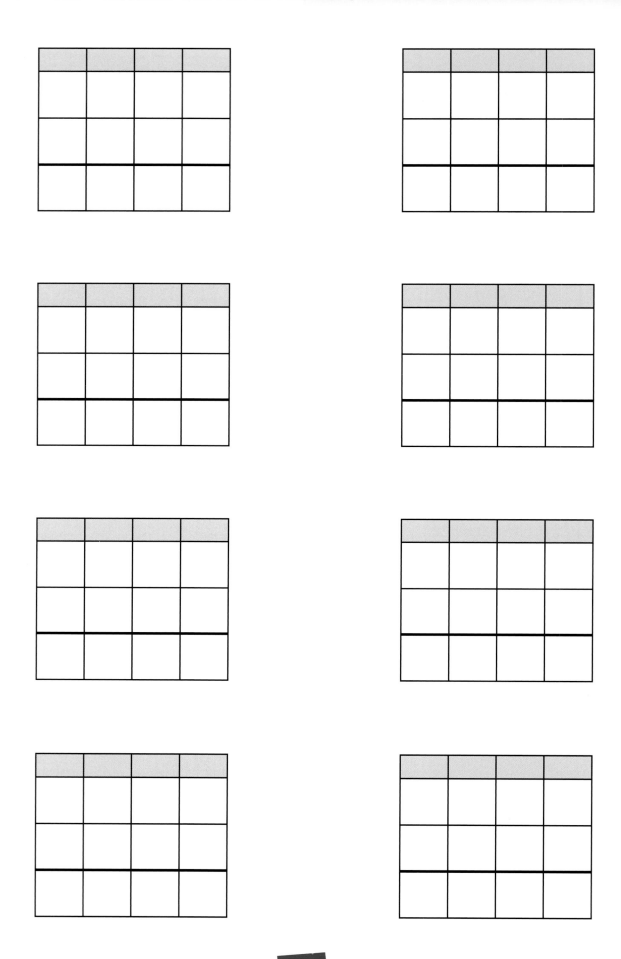

TRY IT

Strategies to Add & Subtract Through 500

Subtraction Strategies

Follow the instructions in the Lesson Guide as you complete this activity page.

1. 250 − 44 = _____

2. 278 − 235 = _____

3. 324 − 63 = _____

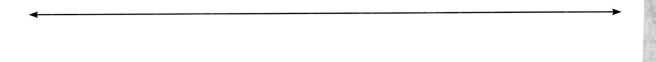

LEARN

Solve each problem by breaking apart the smaller number and counting back. Show your work on the open number line.

4. $419 - 94 =$ _____

5. $205 - 174 =$ _____

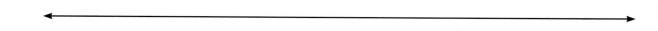

6. $500 - 112 =$ _____

Subtraction Strategies Up Through 500

Practice Ways to Subtract

Solve the subtraction problems the easiest way you can.

1. $375 - 75 =$ _____

2. $435 - 389 =$ _____

3. $500 - 499 =$ _____

4. $375 - 76 =$ _____

5. $888 - 234 =$ _____

6. $375 - 50 =$ _____

7. $422 - 20 =$ _____

8. $462 - 252 =$ _____

L E A R N

Subtraction Strategies Up Through 500

Use Subtraction Strategies

**Solve each problem. Show your work.
Explain how you solved each problem.**

1. 162 − 85 = _____

2. 238 − 170 = _____

3. 295 − 72 = _____

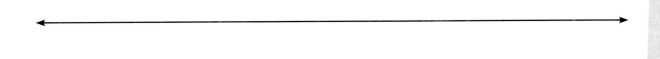

4. 457 − 205 = _____

T R Y I T

Solve each problem.
Explain how you got each answer.

5.   227
        -28

6.   38
        -36

7.   235
        -100

8.   430
        -33

9.   146
        -38

10.   251
         -102

TRY IT

Addition and Subtraction Are Related

Make Addition and Subtraction Simple

Use subtraction to solve each problem. Show your work.

1. $? + 45 = 75$

2. $? + 31 = 55$

Use addition to solve each problem. Show your work.

3. $? - 24 = 33$

4. $? - 72 = 275$

Solve each problem. Show your work.

5. If you know that $25 + 25 = 50$, how could you solve $24 + 25$?

6. If you know that $20 + 20 = 40$, how could you solve $22 + 21$?

TRY IT

Use subtraction to solve each problem. Show your work.

7. $? + 27 = 48$

8. $? + 68 = 79$

Use addition to solve each problem. Show your work.

9. $? - 44 = 44$

10. $? - 156 = 213$

Write the answer.

11. Diana did this subtraction problem.

$67 - 33 = 34$

Write an addition problem she can use to check her work.

Unit Review

Checkpoint Practice

Circle the answer.

1. Paula did this addition problem: $4 + 9 = 13$
    Which subtraction problem shows that she got the answer right?

    A. $6 + 4 = 10$

    B. $4 + 13 = 17$

    C. $13 - 9 = 4$

    D. $13 - 4 = 7$

2. Which of the following can be used to solve this problem?
    $234 + \underline{\hspace{1cm}} = 335$

    A. $335 - 234 = \underline{\hspace{1cm}}$

    B. $200 + 34 = \underline{\hspace{1cm}}$

    C. $335 + 134 = \underline{\hspace{1cm}}$

    D. $200 - 134 = \underline{\hspace{1cm}}$

Write each answer.

3. Write a related addition fact for $19 - 6 = 13$. Explain your answer.

    _____

    _____

    _____

4. Write a related subtraction fact for $5 + 12 = 17$. Explain your answer.

    _____

    _____

    _____

UNIT REVIEW

Circle the answer.

5. Which shows the opposite of the number sentence that this model expresses?

A.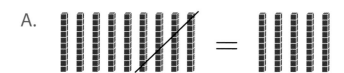

B.

C.

D.

Write each answer.

6. Robert did this subtraction problem: $52 - 17 = 35$
   Write an addition problem he can use to check his work.

   _____

7. Sarah needs to solve $27 + _____ = 50$. Write a subtraction problem she could use to help her solve the addition problem.

   _____

8. How could you use addition to make the problem _____ − 50 = 135 easier to solve?

9. How are addition and subtraction related? Draw a picture or use ones cubes in your explanation.

Solve each problem mentally. Write each answer.

10. $24 + 15 =$ _____

11. $38 - 16 =$ _____

12. $71 - 33 =$ _____

13. $32 + 11 =$ _____

Rewrite problems in the place-value chart and solve.

14. $142 + 205 =$ _____

H	T	O

15. $285 - 124 =$ _____

H	T	O

UNIT REVIEW

Choose a way to solve each problem. Show your work.

16. $360 + 125 = $ _____

17. $358 - 40 = $ _____

Choose a way to solve each problem. Explain how you got your answer.

18. $200 + 165 = $ _____

19.
$$\begin{array}{r} 83 \\ -\ 46 \\ \hline \end{array}$$

Write each answer.

20. If you know that $25 + 75 = 100$, show how you could use that to solve $27 + 74$.

_____

21. Frank solved the addition problem $26 + 28$ in the following way:

Step 1: $26 + 30 = 56$

Step 2: $56 - 2 = 54$

Explain how he solved the problem.

_____

_____

_____

Inches

Measure It

Use your ruler to measure each piece of rope to the nearest inch.

1.

_____ inches

2.

_____ inches

3.

about _____ inches

4.

about _____ inches

Use a square (1 in.) to find each measurement.

5. the length of a spoon

about _____ inches

6. the width of a computer screen

about _____ inches

7. the length of your shoe

about _____ inches

T R Y   I T

Use a square (1 in.) to find each measurement.

8. train of 8 cubes

_____ inches

9. train of 5 cubes

_____ inches

10. 1 tens rod

_____ inches

11. magazine

about _____ inches

12.

_____ inches

Use your ruler to measure each item to the nearest inch.

13. pencil

about _____ inches

14. scissors

about _____ inches

About how long is each item? Measure, and then circle the answer.

15.

| A. about 4 inches | B. about 6 inches |
| C. about 8 inches | D. about 10 inches |

16.

| A. about 4 inches | B. about 6 inches |
| C. about 6 inches | D. about 10 inches |

TRY IT

Centimeters

Measure Length

Use a ruler to measure each item to the nearest centimeter.

1. pencil

   about _____ centimeters

2. paper clip

   about _____ centimeters

3. _____ centimeters

4. _____ centimeters

5.

   A. about 2 centimeters

   B. about 4 centimeters

   C. about 6 centimeters

   D. about 8 centimeters

TRY IT

Use a tens rod (10 cm) to find each measurement to
the nearest centimeter.

6. the length of a fork   about _____ centimeters

7. the width of the computer screen   about _____ centimeters

8. the length of your shoe   about _____ centimeters

9. train of 20 cubes   about _____ centimeters

10.

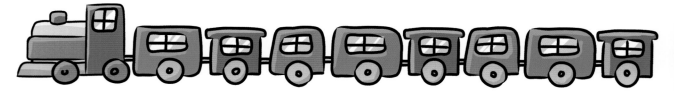

about _____ centimeters

TRY IT

Estimate Length

Estimate in Centimeters

Estimate the length of each object. Then measure to check your estimate.

1.

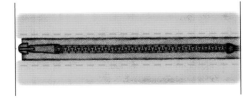

Estimate: about _____ centimeters   Measure: about _____ centimeters

2.

Estimate: about _____ centimeters   Measure: about _____ centimeters

3.

Estimate: about _____ centimeters

Measure: about _____ centimeters

4.

Estimate: about _____ centimeters   Measure: about _____ centimeters

LEARN

5. Estimate the length of an object of your choice.

Name of object: _____

Estimate: about _____ centimeters   Measure: about _____ centimeters

---

Circle the most reasonable estimate.

6. About how long is a pen?

   A. 2 centimeters   B. 15 centimeters   C. 50 centimeters

7. About how long is a toothpick?

   A. 5 centimeters   B. 50 centimeters   C. 100 centimeters

8. About how long is the space bar on a computer keyboard?

   A. 1 centimeter   B. 10 centimeters   C. 90 centimeters

9. About how long is a safety pin?

   A. 2 centimeters   B. 20 centimeters   C. 40 centimeters

10. About how long is a spoon?

   A. 2 centimeters   B. 18 centimeters   C. 80 centimeters

Estimate Length
Make Length Estimates

Estimate the length of each object.

| 1 inch (in.) | 1 centimeter (cm) |

1.

about _____ inches

2.

about _____ inches

3.

about _____ centimeters

4.

about _____ centimeters

107

TRY IT

Circle the most reasonable estimate.

5. About how long is a CD?

    A. 5 inches   B. 25 inches   C. 30 inches   D. 35 inches

6. About how long is a fork?

    A. 1 centimeter   B. 3 centimeters

    C. 20 centimeters   D. 150 centimeters

Circle the answer.

7. Russell measured his pencil to see how long it was. Which of the following is a reasonable estimate for the length of Russell's pencil?

    A. 2 cm   B. 200 cm   C. 15 cm   D. 100 cm

8. Mr. Thomas measured the width of his stove. Which of the following is a reasonable estimate for the width of the stove?

    A. 2 inches   B. 10 inches   C. 30 inches   D. 250 inches

Estimate the length of each object to the nearest inch or centimeter.

9.

about _____ cm

10.

about _____ inches

TRY IT

Compare Measurements

Compare Same Units

Circle Yes if the measures can be compared to each other in the units shown. Circle No if they cannot be compared to each other in the units shown.

1. 6 in. and 8 in.

   A. Yes   B. No

2. 12 cm and 12 in.

   A. Yes   B. No

3. 10 cm and 5 cm

   A. Yes   B. No

Compare. Write <, >, or =.

4. 34 cm _____ 34 cm

5. 14 cm _____ 11 cm

6. 7 in. _____ 21 in.

7. 26 cm _____ 24 cm

8. 8 in. _____ 18 in.

9. 17 in. _____ 39 in.

Answer each question.

10. Brian has a frame that is 26 cm long.
    Dee has a frame that is 16 cm long.

    Who has the longer frame?   _____

11. Anna has a toy that is 32 in. long.
    Tyrone has a toy that is 19 in. long.

    Who has the shorter toy?   _____

L E A R N

Add and Subtract Measurements

Add or subtract to solve.

1. 10 in. + 2 in. = _____ in.

2. 9 cm − 8 cm = _____ cm

3. 8 in. + 2 in. = _____ in.

4. 6 in. − 3 in. = _____ in.

5. 4 cm + 7 cm = _____ cm

6. 7 cm − 5 cm = _____ cm

Answer each question.

7. A juice glass is 4 inches tall.
   A water glass is 8 inches tall.

   How much taller is the water glass than the juice glass?   _____ inches

8. Ria has a pencil that is 10 cm long.
   John has a pencil that is 8 cm long.

   How long are the pencils altogether?   _____ cm

9. Does 12 cm − 7 in. = 5 cm ? Explain.

Compare Measurements

Use Measurements

Underline the nonstandard unit that you will need more of to measure each vegetable. Circle the nonstandard unit you will need fewer of to measure each vegetable.

1.

2.

3.

4.

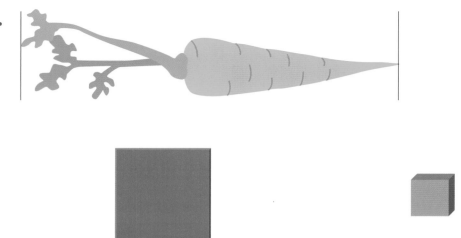

***

Choose the answer for each problem.

5. Jodie measured the width of her bed using centimeters. She then measured her bed again, this time using inches. Which measurement do you think was the bigger number?

   A. the measurement using centimeters

   B. the measurement using inches

   C. both the same

6.

Measure the length of the rectangle with a penny.

How many pennies long is it? _____

If you measured the rectangle with a paper clip, would the measurement be a bigger or smaller number? Why?

   A. bigger   B. smaller

Measure the rectangle with the paper clip to see if you are right.

Circle Yes if the measures can be compared to each other in the units shown. Circle No if they cannot be compared to each other in the units shown.

7. 6 in. and 8 in.

   A. Yes   B. No

8. 12 cm and 7 in.

   A. Yes   B. No

9. 5 cm and 5 cm

   A. Yes   B. No

Compare. Write $<$, $>$, or $=$.

10. 16 cm _____ 10 cm

11. 25 cm _____ 25 cm

12. 9 in. _____ 33 in.

Add or subtract.

13. $9\text{ cm} - 5\text{ cm} = $ _____ cm

14. $5\text{ cm} + 6\text{ cm} = $ _____ cm

Answer each question.

15. Brian has a frame that is 25 in. long.
Dee has a frame that is 18 in. long.
Who has the longer frame? _____

16. John has a card that is 6 in. long.
Jean has a card that is 8 in. long.
How much longer is Jean's card than John's?

17. Chris says that 9 in. is equal to 9 cm. Is Chris correct? Why or why not?

_____

_____

TRY IT

Circle the answer.

18. Does 12 cm − 7 in. = 5 cm?

    A. Yes   B. No

19. Does 10 cm + 5 cm = 15 cm?

    A. Yes   B. No

20. 30 cm − 23 cm = _____

    A. 53 cm   B. 10 cm   C. 7 cm   D. 17 cm

21. 5 in. + 7 in. = _____

    A. 5 in.   B. 7 in.   C. 12 in.   D. 2 in.

22. Sally built a tower that was 12 in. tall and Rachel built one that was 20 in. tall. How much shorter was Sally's tower than Rachel's?

    A. 8 in.   B. 12 in.   C. 22 in.   D. 2 in.

Write the answer.

23. Sandie measured her foot to be 6 inches long.
She then measured her hand to be 4 inches long.

How many inches long are her hand and foot altogether? _____

Compare. Write <, >, or = .

24. 15 in. _____ 16 in.

Read the problem. Explain your answer.

25. Janie says you can add 6 in. and 12 in. to get 18 in.
Do you think this is right? Explain why or why not.

TRY IT

Unit Review

Checkpoint Practice

Use your ruler to measure each pencil to the nearest inch.

1.

about _____ inches

2.

about _____ inches

Use ones cubes to measure the length of the items.

3.

about _____ centimeters

4.

about _____ centimeters

Use the centimeter ruler to find each measurement.

5. the length of a fork

about _____ centimeters

UNIT REVIEW

Use a 1-inch square to find the measurement.

6. the width of a table

about _____ inches

Estimate the length of each object.

7.

about _____ inches

8.

about _____ centimeters

Circle the most reasonable estimate.

9. About how long is a kitchen teaspoon?

A. about 2 inches

B. about 6 inches

C. about 12 inches

D. about 40 inches

Suppose you are asked to measure the fork with the nonstandard units, crayons and paper clips. Will you need more crayons or more paper clips to measure the fork? Circle your answer.

10.

Can the measures be compared to each other in the units shown? Circle Yes or No.

11. 4 in. and 7 in.

Yes   No

12. 12 cm and 10 in.

Yes   No

13. 14 cm and 6 cm

Yes   No

Compare. Choose $<$, $>$, or $=$.

14. 6 in. _____ 12 in.

15. 24 cm _____ 24 cm

16. 11 in. _____ 7 in.

Add or subtract.

17. 6 in. + 2 in. = _____ in.

18. 15 cm − 9 cm = _____ cm

19. A stapler is 24 centimeters long.
A pair of scissors is 18 centimeters long.

How much longer is the
stapler than the pair of scissors?   _____ centimeters

20. Tim has a pencil box that is 10 inches long.
Jill has a pencil box that is 12 inches long.

Who has the shorter pencil box?   _____

21. Look at the picture. Use your ruler to measure the crayon to the nearest inch. How long is the crayon?

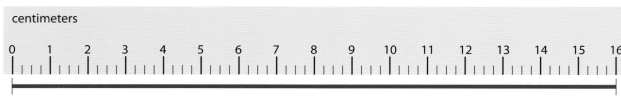

- A. 2 inches
- B. 3 inches
- C. 4 inches
- D. 5 inches

22. Use 1-inch squares to measure the length of a train of 12 cubes. What is the approximate length of the cubes?

about _____ inches

23. Use the tens rods to measure the length of a train of 10 cubes. What is the approximate length of the cubes?

about _____ centimeters

24. How long is the line?

- A. 9 cm
- B. 16 cm
- C. 10 cm
- D. 2 cm

25. Estimate the length of the pencil in centimeters.

about _____ centimeters

26. Mr. Michaels measured the width of his refrigerator. Which of the following is a reasonable estimate for the width of his refrigerator?

- A. 13 inches
- B. 30 inches
- C. 150 inches
- D. 2 inches

27. Patti correctly estimated the length of a paper clip. Which of the following is Patti's estimate?

   A. 1 inch   B. 12 inches

   C. 17 inches   D. 28 inches

28. If you measured the length of the marker by using the ones cube as a unit of length, and then measured the marker by using the paper clip as a unit of length, which statement would be true?

   A. It would take more paper clips than ones cubes to measure the marker.

   B. It would take more ones cubes than paper clips to measure the marker.

   C. It would take the same number of paper clips and ones cubes to measure the marker.

   D. It would take fewer ones cubes than paper clips to measure the marker.

29. Measure the length of the rectangle shown using a paper clip as a unit. If you used a penny to measure the length of the rectangle, would it take more or fewer pennies than paper clips?

_____

_____

30. Which of the following measures can be added together?

　A.　5 cm and 3 in.　　　　　B.　3 in. and 6 cm

　C.　2 in. and 5 in.　　　　　D.　7 in. and 4 cm

31. Patti's cat was playing with some yarn that was 14 in. long.
Sandi's cat was playing with some yarn that was 14 cm long.
Sandi says the two pieces of yarn are the same length.
Do you agree? Explain why or why not.

_____

_____

32. 5 in. + 6 in. = _____

　A.　5 in.　　　　　　　　　B.　11 in.

　C.　6 in.　　　　　　　　　D.　56 in.

33. Eddie had a cheese stick that was 6 in. long. He ate 4 in. of it.
How many inches of the cheese stick are left?

　A.　4 in.　　　　　　　　　B.　6 in.

　C.　2 in.　　　　　　　　　D.　10 in.

34. Which holds more water—a mixing bowl or a cereal bowl?

_____

35. Are there more cups of water in a juice glass or in a saucepan?

_____

Addition Problem-Solving Strategies

Model and Sketch to Add

Sketch the problem. Then solve.

1. Mrs. Bauer bought 3 pounds of red grapes and 4 pounds of green grapes.

   How many pounds of grapes did she buy in all?

   _____ pounds of grapes

2. This summer, Mike read 27 books in all.
   He read 15 books in July and the rest in August.

   How many books did Mike read in August?

   _____ books

TRY IT

3. Pam and Tory collect marbles.
Pam has a bag of 132 marbles.
Tory has a bag of 129 marbles.

How many marbles do they have altogether?

_____ marbles

---

4. Lee had 290 pennies in a jar.
He found some more and put them in the jar.
Now, he has 320 pennies in the jar.

How many pennies did Lee find?

_____ pennies

Addition Problem-Solving Strategies

Addition Sketches

Make a sketch. Then solve each problem.

1. Ed had 15 bouncy balls.
   Tina gave him 6 more.

   How many bouncy balls does Ed have now?

   _____ bouncy balls

2. Rick painted 4 pictures yesterday.
   Today he painted more pictures.
   He painted 7 pictures in all.

   How many pictures did Rick paint today?

   _____ pictures

3. The theater sold 78 adult tickets and 39 child tickets.

   How many tickets did the theater sell in all?

   _____ tickets

TRY IT

4. Mr. Davis had 245 boxes of crayons.
   He ordered 36 more boxes of crayons.

   How many boxes of crayons does Mr. Davis have in all?

   _____ boxes

5. Sue found 45 red rocks and 32 yellow rocks on the beach.

   How many rocks did she find in all?

   _____ rocks

**Use base-10 blocks and a place-value mat to model
and solve the problem.**

6. A pet store has 73 fish in one tank and 66 fish in another tank.

   How many fish are there in the two tanks?

   _____ fish

TRY IT

Subtraction Problem Solving

Sketch and Subtract

Draw a picture to show each problem. Then solve the problem.

1. Nathan has 21 crayons.
   He gives 7 crayons to Carlos.

   How many crayons does Nathan have left?

   _____ crayons in all

   take away _____ crayons   _____ crayons left

2. Jen has 25 coins.
   She puts 18 coins in a coin book.

   How many coins are left?

   _____ coins in all

   take away _____ coins   _____ coins left

3. Wendy has a notebook with 32 pages.
She removes 28 of the pages.

How many pages are left in the notebook?

_____ pages in all

take away _____ pages   _____ pages left

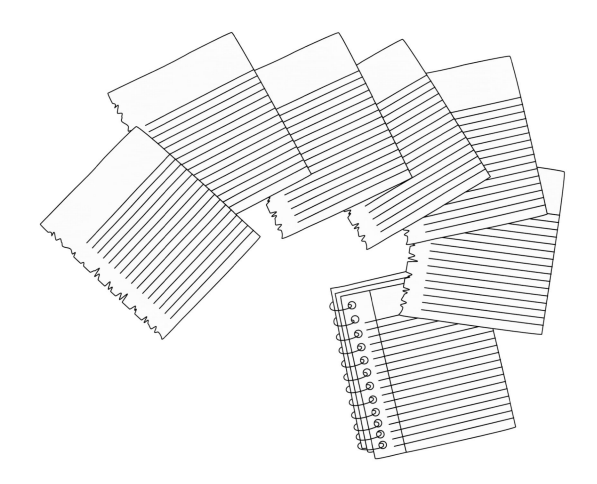

Subtraction Problem Solving

Draw and Solve

Draw a picture. Then solve each problem.

1. Courtney had 9 stickers.
   She gave away 7 stickers.

   How many stickers does Courtney have now?

   _____ stickers in all

   take away _____ stickers   _____ stickers left

2. There were 23 bagels in the box.
   The children ate 16 bagels.

   How many bagels were left?

   _____ bagels in all

   take away _____ bagels   _____ bagels left

Use base-10 blocks to solve.

3. Mandy has 25 postcards.
   She sent 7 postcards to friends.

   How many postcards does Mandy have left?   _____ postcards

TRY IT

SUBTRACTION PROBLEM SOLVING

Use base-10 blocks to solve.

4. Ricardo had 64 markers.
   He put 29 markers away.

   How many markers does Ricardo have left?   _____ markers

5. Mandy had 62 shells.
   She put 40 shells in boxes.

   How many shells does Mandy have left?   _____ shells

Draw a sketch to solve the problem.

6. Maria had 43 stickers.
   She gave her sister 20 stickers.

   How many stickers does she have now? Maria has _____ stickers now.

7. The bookstore had 56 car magazines.
   One weekend the bookstore sold 22 of them.

   How many car magazines
   did the bookstore have left?   There were _____ car magazines left.

Problem Solving
Story Problem Practice

Write a number sentence for each problem. Use a question mark (?) for the missing number. Then solve.

Example: Rob had 27 books.

He bought 12 more books.

How many books does Rob have now?

__27__ $\boxed{+}$ __12__ $\boxed{=}$ __?__ __39__ books

---

1. Mitch has 30 stickers. Rita has 58 stickers.

   How many stickers do they have altogether?

   _____ $\square$ _____ $\square$ _____   _____ stickers

---

2. A jar holds 98 marbles.
   There are 45 striped marbles. The rest are solid.

   How many solid marbles are in the jar?

   _____ $\square$ _____ $\square$ _____   _____ solid marbles

---

3. A toy store has 36 brown teddy bears.
   It has 41 white teddy bears.

   How many teddy bears does the store have altogether?

   _____ $\square$ _____ $\square$ _____   _____ teddy bears

TRY IT

Write a number sentence for each problem. Use a question mark (?) for the missing number. Then solve.

4. Allison has 71 photos.
   There are 40 photos of her family.
   The rest are photos of flowers.

   How many photos of flowers does Allison have?

   _____ flower photos

5. One shelf has 39 books.
   Another shelf has 24 books.

   How many books are on the two shelves?

   _____ books

6. Erin has 20 shirts in her drawer.
   There are 9 shirts with long sleeves, and the rest have short sleeves.

   How many of Erin's shirts have short sleeves?

   _____ shirts with
   short sleeves

TRY IT

Problem Solving with Change

Solve Change Story Problems

Write a number sentence for each problem. Use a question mark (?) for the missing number. Then solve.

Example: Rob had 27 books.

He bought 12 more books.

How many books does Rob have now?

<u>27</u> $\boxed{+}$ <u>12</u> $\boxed{=}$ <u>?</u>   <u>39</u> books

---

1. Tiffany had 16 marbles.
   Peter gave her 22 more marbles.

   How many marbles does Tiffany have now?

   _____ $\boxed{}$ _____ $\boxed{}$ _____   _____ marbles

---

2. Rick had 74 pennies.
   Then he gave 23 pennies to Mary.

   How many pennies does Rick have now?

   _____ $\boxed{}$ _____ $\boxed{}$ _____   _____ pennies

---

3. Garrett had 20 markers.
   Jillian gave him some more markers.
   Now Garrett has 55 markers.

   How many markers did Jillian give him?

   _____ $\boxed{}$ _____ $\boxed{}$ _____   _____ markers

TRY IT

4. Rachel had some stickers.
Then she gave 30 stickers to Sharon.
Now Rachel has 18 stickers.

How many stickers did Rachel start with?

_____ ☐ _____ ☐ _____   _____ stickers

5. Howie had 53 stamps.
Josh gave him some more stamps.
Now Howie has 95 stamps.

How many stamps did Josh give him?

_____ ☐ _____ ☐ _____   _____ stamps

6. Tami had some leaves.
Then she gave 71 leaves to Michael.
Now Tami has 26 leaves.

How many leaves did Tami have at the beginning?

_____ ☐ _____ ☐ _____   _____ leaves

Circle the answer.

7. A gardener had 105 tomatoes.
She gave away 28 tomatoes.

How many tomatoes does she have left?

A. 77   B. 83

C. 87   D. 133

Solve Change Story Problems

Change Problems

Write a number sentence for each problem. Write + or − in the box.
Write the missing numbers and a ? on the correct lines. Then solve.
You may rewrite the problem vertically in the space if needed.

1. Matthew had 129 toy cars.
   He got 12 new cars as gifts.

   How many toy cars does Matthew have now?

    = _____   _____ toy cars

2. Nicole had 264 pretzels.
   She gave 28 pretzels to Alan.

   How many pretzels does Nicole have now?

    = _____   _____ pretzels

3. Jake had some baseball cards.
   Then he gave 15 to Tim.
   Now Jake has 338 baseball cards.

   How many baseball cards did Jake have at the beginning?

    = _____   _____ baseball cards

4. Today, Sam has 125 rocks.
   Yesterday, Rachel gave 27 rocks to Sam.

   How many rocks did Sam have before?

   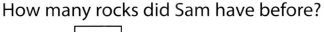 = _____   _____ rocks

T R Y   I T

Circle the answer.

5. Lisa had 218 stickers.
   She gave 39 away.

   How many stickers does she have left?

   A. 227

   B. 257

   C. 179

   D. 127

6. Deana baked 85 cookies.
   Then she baked some more cookies.
   Now Deana has 153 cookies.

   How many more cookies did Deana bake?

   A. 68

   B. 78

   C. 132

   D. 238

Write the answer.

7. Derek had 163 trading cards.
   He bought 21 more trading cards.

   How many trading cards does Derek have now?

   _____ trading cards

8. Syesha had some beads.
   Then she gave 18 to Lana.
   Now Syesha has 205 beads.

   How many beads did Syesha have at the beginning?

   _____ beads

TRY IT

Compare to Solve Story Problems

Compare to Solve

Write a number sentence for each problem. Write a ? for the missing number. Then solve.

1. Emma has 7 hats.
    Shannon has 16 more hats than Emma.

    How many hats does Shannon have?

     = _____   _____ hats

2. Liam collected 15 rocks.
    Evan collected 24 rocks.

    How many more rocks did Evan collect than Liam?

     = _____   _____ rocks

3. Jenny has 36 buttons.
    She has 16 buttons fewer than Deana.

    How many buttons does Deana have?

     = _____   _____ buttons

4. Jason has 48 marbles.
    Cody has 83 marbles.

    How many fewer marbles does Jason have than Cody?

     = _____   _____ marbles

TRY IT

Write the answer.

5. Tom has 12 crayons.
   Jerry has 2 more crayons than Tom.

   How many crayons does Jerry have?

   _____ crayons

6. Geraldine has 127 beads on her necklace.
   Sandra has 27 beads on her necklace.

   How many more beads does Geraldine have
   than Sandra?

   _____ beads

7. Bonnie is baking some cupcakes.
   She wants to decorate each cupcake with a flower.
   She has baked 48 cupcakes and she has 39 flowers.

   How many cupcakes won't get a flower?

   _____ cupcakes

TRY IT

Compare Amounts to Solve Problems

From Words to Number Sentences

Name:

Write a number sentence for each problem. Write a ? for the missing number. Then solve.

1. Erin made 36 pottery bowls.
   Paul made 27 pottery bowls.

   How many fewer bowls did Paul make than Erin?

    _____ bowls

2. Kevin took 248 photos.
   Hailey took 329 photos.

   How many more photos did Hailey take than Kevin?

    _____ photos

3. Paige has 157 drawings.
   Abby has 16 more drawings than Paige.

   How many drawings does Abby have?

    _____ drawings

4. There were 135 masks in the art gallery.
   The art gallery sold 28 masks.

   How many masks are in the art gallery now?

    _____ masks

T R Y   I T

Circle the answer.

5. Lana has 234 trading cards.
   May has 105 trading cards.

   How many more trading cards does Lana have than May?

   A. 339   B. 131   C. 129   D. 239

Write the answer.

6. Shana and Leo are making houses out of building blocks.
   Shana has 53 building blocks.
   She has 23 more building blocks than Leo.

   How many building blocks does Leo have?   _____ building blocks

7. Nick made 28 greeting cards.
   Raul made 19 greeting cards.

   How many fewer greeting cards did Raul
   make than Nick?

   _____ greeting cards

8. Dina has 138 photos.
   Tom has 14 more photos than Dina.

   How many photos does Tom have?   _____ photos

Make Equal Amounts to Solve Problems

Make Equal Groups

Write a number sentence for each problem. Write + or − in the box and ? for the missing number in the number sentence. Then solve.

1. Shannon has 37 beads.
   If she buys 28 more beads, then she will have the same number of beads as Brianna.

   How many beads does Brianna have?

   _____ [ ] _____ = _____   _____ beads

2. Joe has 51 jelly beans.
   If he eats 19 jelly beans, then he will have as many jelly beans as Ricky.

   How many jelly beans does Ricky have?

   _____ [ ] _____ = _____   _____ jelly beans

3. Tyree has 82 paper clips. Jason has 66 paper clips.

   How many paper clips does Tyree have to give away to have as many paper clips as Jason?

   _____ [ ] _____ = _____   _____ paper clips

4. Jessica needs 92 tiles to decorate a tray.
   She has 64 tiles.

   How many more tiles does she need?

   _____ [ ] _____ = _____   _____ tiles

TRY IT

Write a number sentence for each problem. Write + or − in the box and ? for the missing number in the number sentence. Then solve.

5. Ted rode his bike 54 miles.
Jonah rode his bike 88 miles.

How many miles must Ted ride to have ridden the same number as Jonah?

_____ ⬜ _____ = _____   _____ miles

6. Charlotte has 361 marbles.
If she sold 43 marbles, she would have the same number as Violet.

How many marbles does Violet have?

_____ ⬜ _____ = _____   _____ marbles

7. Wallace rode his bike 54 miles.
If he had ridden 40 more miles, he would have ridden the same number of miles as Brady.

How many miles has Brady ridden?

_____ ⬜ _____ = _____   _____ miles

Equalize Story Problems

Outdoor Problems

Write a number sentence for each problem. Write + or − in the box and ? for the missing number in the number sentence. Then solve.

1. Bell Park has 317 trees.
   If the city plants 129 more trees, then it will have planted the same number of trees as Redwood Park.

   How many trees does Redwood Park have?

   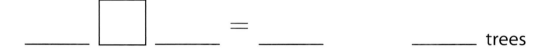

   _____ [ ] _____ = _____   _____ trees

2. Drew and Ivana are collecting pinecones.
   Drew has 241 pinecones.
   If he drops 28 pinecones, then he will have as many pinecones as Ivana.

   How many pinecones does Ivana have?

   _____ [ ] _____ = _____   _____ pinecones

3. Meghan and Peter are selling plant seeds.
   Meghan has 412 seeds.
   Peter has 256 seeds.

   How many seeds does Meghan need to sell to have as many seeds as Peter?

   _____ [ ] _____ = _____   _____ seeds

TRY IT

Write a number sentence for each problem. Write + or − in the box and ? for the missing number in the number sentence. Then solve.

4. Ralph has 227 seeds to plant.
   Wayne has 120 seeds.

   How many seeds does Wayne need to get so he has the same number as Ralph?

   _____ ☐ _____ = _____   _____ seeds

5. Hannah has 58 flowers.
   Thomas has 40 flowers.

   How many flowers does Hannah need to sell to have as many flowers as Thomas?

   _____ ☐ _____ = _____   _____ flowers

Write the answer.

6. Workers at a new park planted 128 rosebushes.
   If the workers were to plant 129 more rosebushes,
   then they would have planted the same number of rosebushes
   as the number of rosebushes in Central Park.

   How many rosebushes does Central Park have?

   _____ rosebushes

Unit Review

Checkpoint Practice

Use base-10 blocks and a place-value mat to solve.

1. The pet store had 257 goldfish. Today the store received a shipment of 140 more goldfish. Which model can be used to show how many goldfish the store has in all?

A.

Hundreds	Tens	Ones

B.

Hundreds	Tens	Ones

C.

Hundreds	Tens	Ones

D.

Hundreds	Tens	Ones

Use base-10 blocks and a place-value mat to solve.

2. Chad has 115 blocks in his collection.
   Ethan has 227 blocks in his collection.

   How many more blocks does Ethan have than Chad?

   _____ more blocks

Read each problem and solve. You may wish to rewrite the problems in vertical format to solve.

3. Anna has 102 crayons in her box.
   Will has 25 crayons in his box.

   How many crayons are there in the two boxes?

   _____ + _____ = _____ crayons

---

4. Curt has 28 bottle caps and Keith has 116 bottle caps.

   How many do they have in all?

   A. 88   B. 144

   C. 154   D. 128

---

5. The farmer had 75 apples in a basket.
   He sold 36 apples.

   How many apples did the farmer have left?

   _____ apples

6. There were 117 bottles of water at the store.
The store sold 89 bottles in one day.

How many bottles of water did the store have then?

A. 28   B. 32   C. 172   D. 206

---

7. Michelle and Christa are collecting buttons.
Michelle has collected 216 buttons.
Christa has collected 110 buttons.

How many more buttons does Christa need to collect to have
the same number of buttons as Michelle?
Write a number sentence and solve.

_____ ☐ _____ = _____

_____ more buttons

---

8. Dale has 274 trading cards.
His friend Harry has 85 trading cards.

How many more trading cards does Dale have than Harry?

A. 111   B. 189

C. 211   D. 359

---

9. Steve and Michele are making a picture book.
Steve has drawn 37 pictures.
He has drawn 15 more pictures than Michele.

How many pictures has Michele drawn?

_____ pictures

10. Brett and Layla are baking cookies.
    Brett has 67 chocolate chips in his bowl.
    He has 27 more chocolate chips than Layla.

    How many chocolate chips does Layla have?
    Write a number sentence and solve.

    _____ chocolate chips

11. Noah and Greg are taking photos.
    Noah took 160 photos and Greg took 238 photos.

    What would Noah have to do to have the same number
    of photos as Greg?

    A. take 68 more photos   B. take 78 more photos

    C. take 138 more photos   D. take 122 more photos

12. Dave and Dash are planting seeds.
    Dave planted 93 seeds and Dash planted 58 seeds.

    How many more seeds would Dash need to plant to have
    the same number as Dave?

    A. 35   B. 45

    C. 141   D. 151

Story Problems

Mixed Story Problems

**Write what is happening in each story. You may draw a sketch.
Then write a number sentence to find the answer.**

1. There are 76 birds in a park. You can see 32 birds on the ground.

    The rest of the birds are hiding in a tree.
    How many birds are hiding in the tree?

    _____

    _____

    _____

    _____ ☐ _____ ☐ _____

    _____ birds

2. The ice cream shop opened this weekend. The shop sold 285 vanilla ice cream cones and 119 chocolate ice cream cones.

    How many cones did the shop sell in all?

    _____

    _____

    _____

    _____ ☐ _____ ☐ _____

    _____ cones

LEARN

3. Jill and Nathan like to collect books.
Nathan has 28 fewer books than Jill.
Nathan has 63 books.

How many books does Jill have?

_____

_____

_____

_____ ☐ _____ ☐ _____

_____ books

---

4. Peter and Lindsey put stickers on their notebooks.
Peter used 37 stickers.
Lindsey used 54 stickers.

How many more stickers did Lindsey use than Peter?

_____

_____

_____

_____ ☐ _____ ☐ _____

_____ stickers

More Story Problems

Solve Story Problems

Write and solve a number sentence for each story problem.

1. Carter has 234 stamps.
Lee has 176 stamps.

How many more stamps does Lee need to have the same number of stamps as Carter?

_____ stamps

2. Billy and Val go to the library together.
Billy reads 96 pages of his book.
Val reads 120 pages of her book.

How many more pages did Val read than Billy?

_____ pages

3. Toby had 114 baseball cards.
His grandfather gave him some boxes of baseball cards.
There were 65 cards in the boxes.

How many cards does Toby have now?

_____ ☐ _____ ☐ _____   _____ cards

TRY IT

Write and solve a number sentence for each story problem.

4. There are 247 dolls on the shelf.
There are 198 dolls in a bin.

How many dolls are there altogether?

_____ ☐ _____ ☐ _____   _____ dolls

5. Roscoe's Bookstore had 482 books for sale.
Customers bought 299 of the books.

How many books were left in the store?

_____ ☐ _____ ☐ _____   _____ books left

6. There are 243 fans cheering for the Wranglers.
There are 222 fans cheering for the Legends.

How many fans are there altogether?

_____ ☐ _____ ☐ _____   _____ fans

7. There are 368 seats in the gym.
If there are 412 people in the gym, how many will not get a seat?

_____ ☐ _____ ☐ _____   _____ people

Problem Solving: Answer Check

Solve and Check

Bror solved these story problems. Solve each problem to check his answer.
If Bror's answer is incorrect, explain what he did wrong.

Example: The puppet show sold 219 tickets on Saturday and 156 tickets on Sunday.

How many tickets did the puppet show sell altogether?

Bror's answer

The puppet show sold 375 tickets altogether.

$$\begin{array}{r} 2\overset{1}{1}9 \\ + 156 \\ \hline 375 \end{array}$$

Yes. Bror is correct.

---

1. On a nature hike, Mike saw 39 alligators. Lisa saw 24 alligators.

   How many more alligators did Mike see?

   Bror's answer

   Mike saw 63 alligators in all.

2. Jasmine scored 98 points on a math game. Kirk scored 77 points.

How many points did they score in all?

Bror's answer

They scored 165 points in all.

---

3. Jenny saw 354 beetles on her grandfather's farm.
She saw 138 at his house.

How many more beetles did she see on the farm?

Bror's answer

Jenny saw 216 more beetles on the farm.

---

4. Lee read for 228 minutes last month.
This month she read for 179 minutes.

How many minutes did Lee read altogether?

Bror's answer

Lee read for 49 minutes altogether.

Problem Solving: Answer Check

Is the Answer Correct?

Tell if each answer is correct. Write Yes or No.
If no, explain why and give the correct answer.

1. **Problem**
   Eileen had 277 stickers in her collection. She got 125 more stickers for her birthday.

   How many stickers does she have now?

   Answer
   Eileen has 392 stickers now.

   $$\begin{array}{r} 277 \\ +125 \\ \hline 392 \end{array}$$

   Is the answer correct? _____

2. **Problem**
   At the beginning of the circus, the clown had 45 balloons.
   By the end, 13 of the balloons had popped.

   How many balloons did **not** pop?

   Answer
   32 balloons did not pop.

   $$\begin{array}{r} 45 \\ -13 \\ \hline 32 \end{array}$$

   Is the answer correct? _____

3. **Problem**
   Nicki put 264 marbles in a jar.
   Justin put 132 marbles in a bag.

   How many marbles do they have altogether?

   Answer
   They have 132 marbles altogether.

   $$\begin{array}{r} 264 \\ -132 \\ \hline 132 \end{array}$$

   Is the answer correct? _____

TRY IT

Read each problem and check the answer.
Circle Correct or Incorrect.

4. Problem

A supermarket sold 168 cans of tuna last week.
This week the supermarket sold 105 cans of tuna.

How many cans of tuna did the supermarket sell in all?

Answer
The supermarket sold 273 cans of tuna in all.

A. Correct B. Incorrect

5. Problem

On Tuesday a baker made 60 pies.
On Wednesday he made 24 pies.

How many more pies did he make on Tuesday than on Wednesday?

Answer
He made 46 more pies on Tuesday than on Wednesday.

A. Correct B. Incorrect

6. Problem

The pet store has 157 brown mice.
It has 326 white mice.

How many more white mice does the pet store have than brown mice?

Answer
It has 231 more white mice.

A. Correct B. Incorrect

TRY IT

Explain Problem Solutions

Explain Solutions

**Circle whether you would add or subtract to solve each problem.
Then explain your choice.**

1. The movie store rented 321 movies on Saturday
   and 145 movies on Sunday.

   How many more movies were rented on Saturday than on Sunday?

   Add   Subtract

---

2. Lisa read 198 pages.
   Trisha read 133 pages.

   How many more pages does Trisha need to read to have read
   as many pages as Lisa?

   Add   Subtract

Solve each problem. Use sketches or diagrams to help.

3. The square jar has 227 gumballs.
   The round jar has 162 gumballs.

   How many gumballs are in both jars?

   _____gumballs

---

4. The clown has 77 balloons.
   He gave away 24 balloons.

   Now how many balloons does he have?

   _____ balloons

T R Y   I T

Circle the answer that best explains how you could solve the problem.

5. Clara sewed 77 patches onto her quilt in the morning.
   Then in the afternoon, she sewed on 43 more patches.

   How many patches did Clara sew in all?

   A. You have to find the total number of patches that Clara sewed, so you should add 77 and 43.

   B. Subtract 43 from 77 to find the difference in how many patches were sewed.

   C. You have to find out how many more patches Clara needs to sew, so you should subtract.

6. At a bake sale, Bryan has sold 54 cupcakes.
   At the next table, Gerry has sold 67.

   How many more cupcakes must Bryan sell if he wants to sell as many cupcakes as Gerry?

   A. Subtract 54 from 67 to find the difference between the number of cupcakes sold by Bryan and Gerry.

   B. Add 54 and 57 to find the difference between the number of cupcakes sold by Bryan and Gerry.

   C. Add 54 and 67 to find the total number of cupcakes sold by Bryan and Gerry.

Explain how to solve each problem. Tell how you decided whether to add or subtract. Circle your answer.

7. Marco has 108 toothpicks.
   He has 28 more toothpicks than Ria.

   How many toothpicks does Ria have?

   Add   Subtract

8. The toy store got a delivery of 346 new action figures.
   The store sold 99 action figures in one day.

   How many action figures are left in the store?

   Add   Subtract

Justify Procedures Selected

Solve and Justify

**Write the number sentence that solves each story problem.
Then tell why you solved the problem as you did, and explain
why your solution makes sense.**

1. Amy's book has 265 pages.
   Amy has read 189 pages so far.

   How many more pages does she need to read
   to finish the book?

   _____

2. There are 74 butterflies and 92 caterpillars.

   How many more caterpillars are there than butterflies?

   _____

3. There were 63 pretzels on the shelf.
   The baker put 48 more pretzels on the shelf.

   How many pretzels are on the shelf now?

   _____

4. Hector planted 141 red flowers and 85 white flowers.

   How many flowers did Hector plant in all?

   _____

T R Y   I T

Tell how you would solve each problem and explain why your solution makes sense.

5. There were 25 pencils in a box.
Then 10 pencils fell out of the box.

How many pencils were left in the box?

6. The Salty Sea Shop sold 87 shells in June.
The shop sold 32 shells in July.

How many more shells did the shop sell in June than in July?

7. Sandro has washed 26 cars.
His friend Tomas has washed 44 cars.

How many more cars does Sandro need to wash if he wants to wash as many cars as Tomas did?

8. Harry wrote the number sentence $145 + 43 = 188$ to solve the following problem.

Marla has 145 leaves in her collection.
Barb has 43 leaves in her collection.

How many leaves do they have altogether?

Is Harry's number sentence correct for solving this problem? Explain your answer.

TRY IT

Justify Solutions

Justify and Solve Problems

Circle Add or Subtract to show how you would solve each problem. Then tell why you would add or subtract.

1. Mike took 250 photos at the air show.
   Jake took 125 photos.

   How many more photos did Mike take than Jake?

   Add   Subtract

2. The circus sold 330 tickets on Saturday.
   On Sunday morning, it sold 180 tickets.

   How many more tickets did the circus need to sell on Sunday to equal the number of tickets sold on Saturday?

   Add   Subtract

3. The concert organizer printed 450 programs and gave out 320 programs.

   How many programs were left?

   Add   Subtract

4. The food stand sold 172 lemon ice drinks and 212 strawberry ice drinks.

   How many ice drinks were sold in all?

   Add   Subtract

5. Frances read 16 books last year.
   This year she read 42 books.

   How many books did she read in all?

   Add   Subtract

T R Y   I T

6. Tom had 30 balloons.
He gave 14 balloons to his sister.

How many balloons does Tom have left?

Add   Subtract

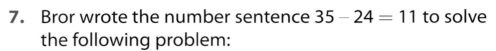

---

7. Bror wrote the number sentence 35 − 24 = 11 to solve the following problem:

Yolanda is putting hoses together to make a longer hose, and so is Sarah.
If Yolanda's hose is 35 feet long and Sarah's is only 24 feet long, how many more feet must be added to Sarah's hose if she wants to have a hose as long as Yolanda's?

Is Bror's number sentence correct to use when solving this problem? Circle Yes or No. Explain your answer.

Yes   No

---

8. Boris's camping shop sold 254 tents one summer.
The next summer the shop sold 321 tents.

How many more tents did Boris sell in the second summer?

Circle the answer that best explains how you could correctly solve this problem.

A. Add 254 and 321 to find the total number of tents sold.

B. Add 254 and 321 to find the difference of the numbers of tents sold.

C. Subtract 254 from 321 to find the difference of the numbers of tents sold.

Create Story Problems

Make Up Problems

1. Make up one addition story problem using the numbers 385 and 497.
   Use a ? for the missing number.

   _____

   _____

   _____

   _____ ☐ _____ ☐ _____

2. Make up one subtraction story problem using the numbers 385 and 497.
   Use a ? for the missing number.

   _____

   _____

   _____

   _____ ☐ _____ ☐ _____

TRY IT

3. Make up one addition story problem using the numbers 286 and 207. Use a ? for the missing number.

_____

_____

_____

_____ ☐ _____ ☐ _____

4. Make up one subtraction story problem using the numbers 286 and 207. Use a ? for the missing number.

_____

_____

_____

_____ ☐ _____ ☐ _____

TRY IT

Make Your Own Story Problems

Create Story Problems

Make up a story problem for each number sentence using the information in the picture of the toy store.

| 107 cars | 294 trucks | 316 games | 275 puzzles | 381 dolls |

1. $294 + 107 = ?$

_____

_____

_____

2. $316 - 275 = ?$

_____

_____

_____

TRY IT

Use the picture on the front to write a story problem for the given operation. Write a matching number sentence. Use a ? for the missing number.

3. Subtraction.

_____

_____

_____ ☐ _____ ☐ _____

Write a story problem using the numbers and given operation. Write a matching number sentence. Use a ? for the missing number.

4. 230 and 60. Subtraction.

_____

_____

_____ ☐ _____ ☐ _____

5. 145 and 200. Addition.

_____

_____

_____ ☐ _____ ☐ _____

TRY IT

Similar Story Problems
Classify Problems

 The Crayon Problem

There are 100 boxes of crayons on the shelf.
There are 144 boxes of crayons in a cart.

How many boxes of crayons are there in all?
$100 + 144 = ?$

 The Jacket Problem

There are 25 green jackets.

There are 13 yellow jackets.

How many more green jackets are there than yellow jackets?
$25 - 13 = ?$

For Problems 1–6, write a number sentence for each problem. If the problem is like the Crayon Problem, circle the crayon. If the problem is like the Jacket Problem, circle the jacket.

1. Austin has 168 stamps.
    He buys 42 more stamps.

    How many stamps does he have now?

    _____

2. Kaitlyn has 68 stickers.
    Nicole has 52 stickers.

    How many more stickers does Kaitlyn have than Nicole?

    _____

3. Kim has 56 shells.
    Jake has 82 shells.

    How many more shells does Kim have to find to have as many shells as Jake?

    _____

4. There are 203 pencils in a red box and 171 pencils in a yellow box.

    How many pencils are there altogether?

    _____

T R Y   I T

5. A theater sold 319 tickets on Saturday and 196 tickets on Sunday.

How many tickets did they sell altogether?

_____

6. There are 289 pretzel sticks and 122 juice boxes.

How many fewer juice boxes are there than pretzel sticks?

_____

7. Can Problem A be solved in the same way as Problem B? Circle Yes or No. Write why.

A	**B**
Jeff has 48 pennies. Susie has 120 more pennies than Jeff. How many pennies does Susie have?	Ben visits the craft store and spends $54 on paint and $43 on modeling clay. How much does he spend in all?

   A. Yes   B. No

_____

8. Frank has 16 marbles and George has 20 marbles.

How many more marbles does George have than Frank?

Here is a number sentence that solves this problem: $20 - 16 = 4$.

Circle the problem that could be solved in the same way.

A. Tyler has 8 more comic books than Bernie.
Bernie has 12 comic books.

How many comic books does Tyler have?

B. Diane has 7 pairs of shoes and Tara has 12 pairs of shoes.

How many fewer pairs of shoes does Diane have than Tara?

Name:

 The Ribbon Problem

The art club needs 215 yards of ribbon.
It has 99 yards so far.

How many more yards does the club need?
$99 + ? = 215$

 The Stair Problem

There are 100 stairs in the fire station.
A firefighter climbed some stairs and stopped.
Then he climbed the other 87 stairs.

How many stairs did he climb before stopping?
$? + 87 = 100$

For Problems 1–4, write a number sentence for each problem. If the problem is like the Ribbon Problem, circle the ribbon. If the problem is like the Stair Problem, circle the stairs.

1. Mrs. Rose bought 174 flowers.
She bought some tulips.
She bought 89 daisies.

   How many tulips did she buy?

   _____

2. A book is 268 pages long.
Tyler has read 179 pages.

   How many more pages does Tyler need to read to finish the book?

   _____

3. It is 163 miles from Bridget's house to Greenville.
She has driven 77 miles so far.

   How many more miles must Bridget drive to reach Greenville?

   _____

4. The squirrel hid 165 nuts.
He hid some small nuts.
He hid 92 large nuts.

   How many small nuts did the squirrel hide?

   _____

T R Y   I T

5. Roger had some paper plates for the school picnic. He bought 134 more. He now has 346 plates.

How many plates did Roger have at the beginning?

Circle the story problem that could be solved in the same way.

A. Allyson had lots of books. She bought 26 new books. She now has 237 books.

How many books did she start with?

B. Mike had 254 bottle caps. He found 123 more bottle caps.

How many bottle caps does Mike have now?

6. Can Problem A be solved in the same way as Problem B? Circle Yes or No. Tell why.

A	B
Kenta had many treats for his dog. He bought 153 more treats. Kenta now has 421 treats.	In August, a bike store sold 243 bikes. It sold 312 bikes in September.
How many treats did he have before he bought more treats?	How many bikes did the bike store sell in 2 months?

A. Yes

B. No

7. Read the following story problem. Then write a problem that could be solved in the same way.

The library had 399 books about dogs.

The library bought more books about dogs and now has 436.

How many books did the library buy?

_____

_____

_____

TRY IT

Unit Review

Checkpoint Practice

Write the number sentence that solves each story problem.
Then tell why you solved the problem as you did.

1. Corkey the Clown sells balloons at the circus.
He sold 76 red balloons and 91 blue balloons.

   How many more blue balloons did Corkey sell than red balloons?

   _____

   _____

   _____

2. There are 311 beads in a box.
There are 125 beads in a bag.

   How many beads are there altogether?

   _____

   _____

   _____

UNIT REVIEW

Tell if each answer is correct. If an answer is **not** correct, explain why and give the correct answer.

3. **Problem**

Josie had 425 beads.
She used 137 beads to make necklaces for her friends.

How many beads does Josie have left?

Student's answer
Josie has 312 beads left.

Is this answer correct?

_____

_____

_____

4. **Problem**

Erwin has 178 stamps in his collection.
His grandfather gave him 54 more stamps.

How many stamps does Erwin have now?

Student's answer
Erwin has 124 stamps now.

Is this answer correct?

_____

_____

_____

Follow the instructions for each problem.

5. Write one addition story problem and one subtraction story problem with the numbers 218 and 350. Write a number sentence for each story, and use a ? for the missing number.

Addition Story Problem

_____

_____

_____

_____

Subtraction Story Problem

_____

_____

_____

_____

6. Read the two story problems. Write the number sentence that you can use to solve each problem.

Chris is playing a computer game.
He needs 500 points to move to the next level.
So far he has scored 372 points.

How many more points does Chris need
to score to move to the next level? _____

There are 315 seats in the cafeteria.
At lunch there were 197 people.

How many cafeteria seats were empty? _____

Are the two problems similar? _____

Tell why or why not.

_____

_____

_____

_____

_____

_____

7. Write a number sentence that you could use to solve this problem, and then solve.

   Tony worked on the crossword puzzle for 10 fewer minutes than Anna did.
   Anna worked on the crossword puzzle for 25 minutes.

   How many minutes did Tony spend working on the crossword puzzle?

   _____

   Tony worked for _____ minutes.

8. How would you solve the following problem? Tell how you decided whether to add or to subtract.

   Problem: Mickey got a new bag of 180 building blocks and now he has 412 blocks.
   Mickey already had some blocks.

   How many blocks did Mickey have to begin with?

9. Bror wrote the number sentence $38 - 28 = 10$ to solve the following problem:

   Jared scored 38 points in the basketball game.
   John scored 28 points in the basketball game.

   How many more points would John need to score to have the same number of points as Jared?

   Is Bror's number sentence correct to use when solving this problem? Circle Yes or No. Then explain your answer.

   A. Yes   B. No

10. Vince solved the following story problem. Check his answer and decide whether it is correct or incorrect.

Problem
The grocery store had 241 boxes of cereal.
More boxes of cereal were delivered to the store, and the store now has 402 boxes.

How many boxes of cereal were delivered to the store?

Vince's answer
261 boxes of cereal were delivered to the store.

A. Correct   B. Incorrect

---

11. Leona solved this story problem. Check her answer and decide whether it is correct or incorrect.

Problem
Jane counted 346 stars.
She counted 58 fewer stars than Meena did.

How many stars did Meena count?

Leona's answer
Meena counted 394 stars.

A. Correct   B. Incorrect

---

12. Which number sentence could you use to solve the following problem?

The Lazy Daisy Café has 120 seats.
At lunchtime there are 37 seats filled.

How many seats in the café are empty?

A. $120 + 37 = ?$

B. $120 - 37 = ?$

C. $120 + 83 = ?$

D. $37 + 37 = ?$

13. Can Problem A be solved in the same way as Problem B?
Circle Yes or No. Then explain your answer.

A	**B**
Frances gave 16 cookies to her neighbors. Now Frances has 12 cookies left. How many cookies did Frances have in the beginning?	Harriet's mom drove 6 miles to the store and then drove 12 miles to the post office. How many miles did she drive altogether?

A.   Yes

B.   No

---

14. Can Problem A be solved in the same way as Problem B?
Circle Yes or No. Then explain your answer.

A	**B**
Fiona has 26 pears. If she gives away 12 pears, she will have the same number as Nina. How many pears does Nina have?	Jason had 56 marbles. He gave some to Frank. Now Jason has 33 marbles. How many marbles did he give to Frank?

A.   Yes

B.   No

15. Write a story problem with the numbers 66 and 32 that can be solved by using addition. Then write an addition sentence to solve the problem.

_____

_____

_____

_____

16. Write a story problem with the numbers 120 and 15 that can be solved by using subtraction. Then write a subtraction sentence to solve the problem.

_____

_____

_____

_____

Semester Review

Checkpoint Practice

Read each problem and follow the directions.

1. The clocks show the times when Lucas begins and ends his soccer practice. How long does his practice last?

_____ hours

2. Write numbers on the lines to write ten dollars.

   $ _____ _____.00

3. Write a related addition number sentence for $22 - 10 = 12$.

   _____

4. Add mentally.

   $65 + 32 = ?$

   A. 83

   B. 87

   C. 93

   D. 97

5. Use your ruler to measure the length of your spoon to the nearest inch. Write the length.

   _____ inches

6. How long is the line?

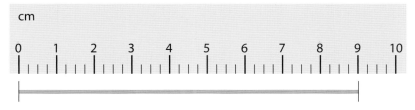

   A. 9 cm

   B. 6 cm

   C. 8 cm

   D. 7 cm

7. Find the sum.

$255 + 179 =$ _____

A. 434

B. 324

C. 176

D. 424

8. Find the difference.

$$
\begin{array}{r}
193 \\
-\ 105 \\
\hline
\end{array}
$$

A. 72

B. 93

C. 67

D. 88

9. Which other number sentence can you use to solve the problem below?

$126 - 12 = ?$

A. $120 + 26 - 12$

B. $110 + 16 - 12$

C. $110 + 26 + 12$

D. $10 - 12$

10. These base-10 blocks show the number 150. Use your base-10 blocks to show another way that you can make 150.

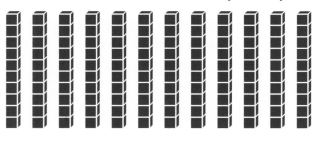 

11. What is the value of the underlined number?

23<u>6</u>

A. 600

B. 60

C. 6

12. Use base-10 blocks to model and solve this problem.

$$
\begin{array}{r}
119 \\
+\ 222 \\
\hline
\end{array}
$$

13. Use base-10 blocks to model and solve this problem.

$$
\begin{array}{r}
458 \\
-\ 139 \\
\hline
\end{array}
$$

14. Use the base-10 blocks and place-value mat to solve.

Marla had some stickers.
Her sister gave her 61 more.
Now Marla has 273 stickers.

How many stickers did Marla start with? _____ stickers

---

15. Jay has 46 marbles and Kay has 117 marbles.

How many marbles do they have in all?

A. 71   B. 146   C. 153   D. 163

---

16. There were 112 fish in a fish store.
The store sold 65 fish in one day.

How many fish did the store have left?

A. 53   B. 47   C. 153   D. 177

---

17. Cindy has 283 songs saved on her computer.
Her friend Rita has 97 songs on her computer.

How many more songs does Cindy have than Rita?

A. 186   B. 206   C. 214   D. 380

---

18. Pam and Sam wrote about their families.
Pam wrote 150 words and Sam wrote 212 words.

What would Pam have to do to have the same number of words as Sam?

A. Write 62 more words.   B. Write 112 more words.

C. Erase 112 of her words.   D. Write 142 more words.

---

19. Write and solve a number sentence to solve the following problem.

There are 243 fans cheering for the Wranglers.
There are 222 fans cheering for the Legends.

How many fans are there altogether?

_____

20. Read the problem below.

Frances read 16 books last year.
This year she read 42 books.

How many books did she read in all?

How would you solve this problem? Why would you solve it that way?

_____

_____

21. Use the numbers 54 and 17 to write a story problem that can be solved with addition.

Then write an addition sentence to solve the problem.

_____

_____

_____

22. Compare. Choose $<$, $>$, or $=$.

365 _____ 375

A. $<$ B. $>$ C. $=$

23. Order the numbers 257, 476, and 313 from least to greatest, by using the symbols $<$ or $>$.

_____

24. Order the numbers 184, 144, and 164 from greatest to least, by using the symbols $<$ or $>$.

_____

Write Number Words Through 1,000

Practice Writing Number Words

Write the number in word form.

1. 486

_____

2. 213

_____

3. 1,000

_____

4. 841

_____

5. 570

_____

6. 304

_____

TRY IT

647 1,000 570
985

7. 719

_____

8. 647

_____

9. 612

_____

10. 985

_____

11. 215

_____

12. 861

_____

Represent Numbers Through 1,000
Practice Showing Numbers

Circle the blocks you would use to show the number.

1. 251

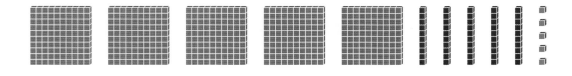

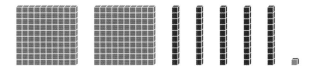

2. 864

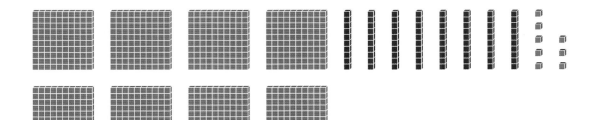

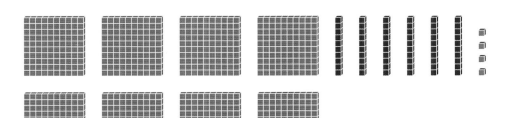

183

TRY IT

3. 431

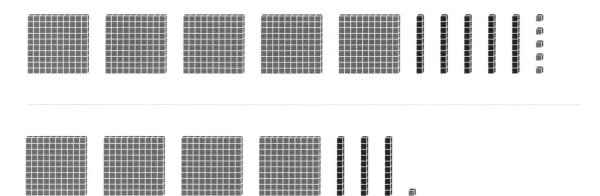

4. 113

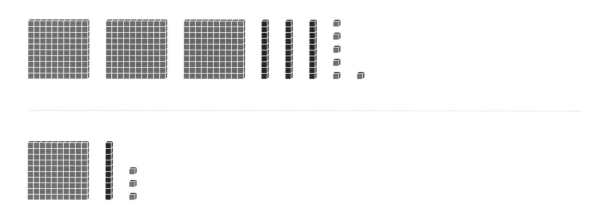

TRY IT

Work with Numbers Through 1,000

Represent Numbers Through 1,000

Read the problem and follow the directions.

1. Write the number shown by the base-10 blocks.

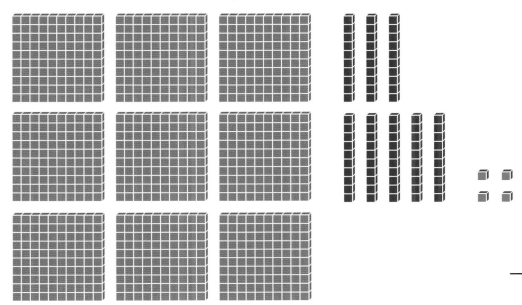

_____

2. Circle the group of base-10 blocks that shows 618.

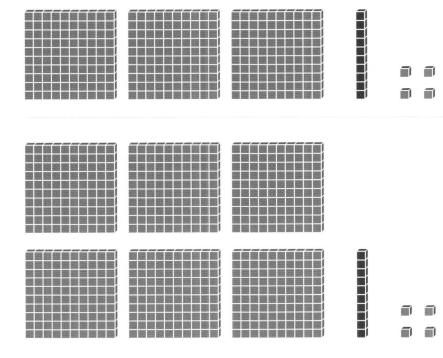

T R Y I T

3. How many hundreds are in 407?

_____

4. If you have 2 hundreds, 6 tens, and 9 ones, what number do you have?

_____

Circle the answer.

5. Which is another way to show 200 + 40 + 8?

A. 248   B. 204   C. 208

6. Which is the same as 537?

A. 7 hundreds, 3 tens, 5 ones

B. 50 hundreds, 3 tens, 7 ones

C. 5 hundreds, 3 tens, 7 ones

7. What is the value of the 9 in 493?

A. 9

B. 90

C. 900

8. What is the value of the 9 in 917?

A. 9

B. 90

C. 900

9. Which digit is in the tens place in the number 345?

A. 3

B. 4

C. 5

TRY IT

Model Numbers Through 1,000

Models and Groups

Read the problem and follow the directions.

1. Write the number that the blocks show.

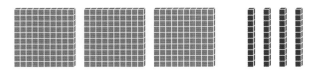

_____

2. Circle the blocks that show 960.

A.

B.
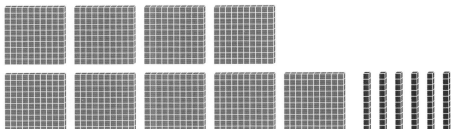

3. Circle the blocks that show 703.

A.
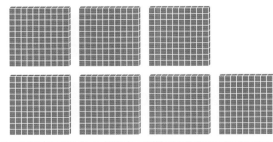

B.
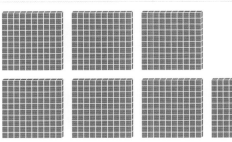

T R Y   I T

Circle the answer.

4. Which group equals 401?

   A. 4 hundreds, 1 ten, 0 ones

   B. 4 hundreds, 0 tens, 1 one

   C. 4 hundreds, 1 ten, 1 one

5. Which group equals 809?

   A. 8 hundreds, 9 tens, 0 ones

   B. 8 tens, 9 ones

   C. 8 hundreds, 0 tens, 9 ones

6. Which number does $200 + 40 + 1$ show?

   A. 204

   B. 201

   C. 241

7. Which number does $600 + 20 + 0$ show?

   A. 602

   B. 620

   C. 62

8. Which number has 6 hundreds?

   A. 56

   B. 189

   C. 654

   D. 346

9. Which number has 9 tens?

   A. 59

   B. 98

   C. 19

   D. 9

Write the answer.

10. How many hundreds, tens, and ones are in 608?

    _____

11. How many hundreds, tens, and ones are in 250?

    _____

TRY IT

Practice Place Value

Circle the digit for the named place.

1. tens

735

2. ones

932

3. hundreds

183

4. hundreds

794

5. ones

561

6. thousands

1,000

268

156

98

965

TRY IT

Write which place the 5 is in for the number.

7. 852

_____

8. 503

_____

9. 395

_____

10. 950

_____

Write which place the 1 is in for the number.

11. 316

_____

12. 451

_____

13. 127

_____

14. 1,000

_____

Circle the value of the underlined digit.

15. <u>3</u>57

3   30   300

16. 72<u>4</u>

4   40   400

17. 9<u>1</u>2

1   10   100

TRY IT

Write the value of the underlined digit.

18. 2<u>3</u>4

_____

19. <u>6</u>91

_____

20. <u>1</u>,000

_____

21. 59<u>2</u>

_____

22. <u>9</u>25

_____

23. 8<u>5</u>1

_____

24. 1<u>6</u>3

_____

25. 99<u>9</u>

_____

Circle the digit for the named place.

26. ones

582

27. hundreds

615

28. thousands

1,000

29. tens

882

TRY IT

Circle the answer.

30. In which place is the 7 in the number?

791

A. thousands

B. hundreds

C. tens

D. ones

985

512

31. In which place is the 4 in the number?

498

A. thousands

B. hundreds

C. tens

D. ones

159

1,000

32. Which digit is in the hundreds place in the number?

597

A. 5

B. 9

C. 7

Standard to Expanded Form

Practice Expanded Form

Use numbers and words to write the number in expanded form.

Example: $267 = \underline{\quad 2 \quad}$ hundreds $+ \underline{\quad 6 \quad}$ tens $+ \underline{\quad 7 \quad}$ ones

1. $842 = \underline{\qquad}$ hundreds $+ \underline{\qquad}$ tens $+ \underline{\qquad}$ ones

2. $604 = \underline{\qquad}$ hundreds $+ \underline{\qquad}$ tens $+ \underline{\qquad}$ ones

3. $519 = \underline{\qquad}$ hundreds $+ \underline{\qquad}$ tens $+ \underline{\qquad}$ ones

4. $370 = \underline{\qquad}$ hundreds $+ \underline{\qquad}$ tens $+ \underline{\qquad}$ ones

5. $1,000 = \underline{\qquad}$ thousands $+ \underline{\qquad}$ hundreds $+ \underline{\qquad}$ tens $+ \underline{\qquad}$ ones

Circle the expanded form of the number.

6. **975**
   A. $900 + 70 + 5$
   B. $900 + 700 + 5$
   C. $9 + 7 + 5$
   D. $90 + 75$

7. **718**
   A. $7 + 1 + 8$
   B. $700 + 10 + 8$
   C. $700 + 18 + 8$
   D. $7 + 18$

TRY IT

Use only numbers to write the number in expanded form.

Example: 937 = __900__ + __30__ + __7__

8. 756 = _____ + _____ + _____

9. 491 = _____ + _____ + _____

10. 843 = _____ + _____ + _____

11. 620 = _____ + _____ + _____

12. 506 = _____ + _____ + _____

Write the answer.

13. What is 550 written in expanded form?

_____ hundreds + _____ tens + _____ ones

14. Write the number 301 in expanded form.

_____

TRY IT

Expanded to Standard Form

Expanded Form to Standard Form

Write the number in standard form.

1. 5 hundreds + 9 tens + 1 one = _____

2. 7 hundreds + 2 tens + 7 ones = _____

3. 1 thousand + 0 hundreds + 0 tens + 0 ones = _____

4. 4 hundreds + 5 tens + 3 ones = _____

5. 3 hundreds + 0 tens + 1 one = _____

6. 800 + 60 + 0 = _____

7. 600 + 10 + 8 = _____

8. 900 + 30 + 2 = _____

9. 400 + 0 + 5 = _____

TRY IT

Circle the expanded form.

10.

200

A. 2 hundreds + 0 tens + 0 ones

B. 200 hundreds + 0 tens + 0 ones

C. 2 hundreds + 2 tens + 2 ones

D. 20 hundreds + 0 tens + 0 ones

11.

619

A. 9 hundreds + 1 ten + 6 ones

B. 900 hundreds + 10 tens + 6 ones

C. 600 hundreds + 10 tens + 9 ones

D. 6 hundreds + 1 ten + 9 ones

Write the number in expanded form.

12.

200

_____ hundreds + _____ tens + _____ ones

13.

401

_____ hundreds + _____ tens + _____ ones

TRY IT

Compare and Order Numbers

Practice Comparing and Ordering

Compare the numbers. Write <, >, or =.

1. 578 ☐ 579

2. 743 ☐ 734

3. 617 ☐ 617

4. 872 ☐ 695

5. 935 ☐ 917

6. 669 ☐ 686

7. 803 ☐ 803

8. 993 ☐ 1,000

Order the numbers. Write <, >, or =.

9. 682 ☐ 687 ☐ 688

10. 519 ☐ 518 ☐ 511

11. 709 ☐ 710 ☐ 731

12. 522 ☐ 528 ☐ 540

TRY IT

Write the numbers in order from least to greatest. Use <.

13. 725, 735, 705

_____ ☐ _____ ☐ _____

14. 567, 564, 569

_____ ☐ _____ ☐ _____

Write the numbers in order from greatest to least. Use >.

15. 957, 955, 959

_____ ☐ _____ ☐ _____

16. 675, 499, 522

_____ ☐ _____ ☐ _____

Compare. Circle >, <, or =.

17. 682 ? 561

    A. <

    B. >

    C. =

18. 798 ? 741

    A. <

    B. >

    C. =

Name:

Say the answer.

1. Count aloud from 810 to 820.

2. Say the missing numbers.

    699, 700, _____, _____, 703, 704

Write the number in word form.

3. 599 _____

4. 824 _____

5. 803 _____

6. 1,000 _____

UNIT REVIEW

Circle the blocks you would use to show the number.

7. 235

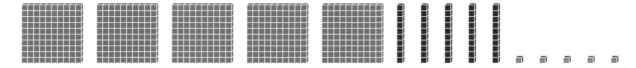

8. 749

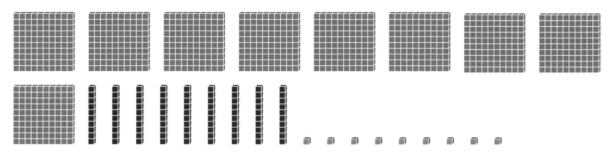

9. 142

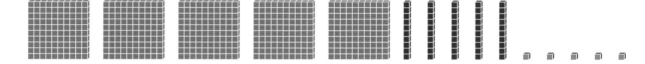

Circle the answer.

10. What number is modeled?

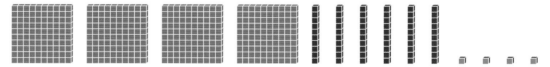

    A. 446

    B. 466

    C. 464

11. What number is modeled?

7 hundreds, 9 tens, 2 ones

    A. 792

    B. 297

    C. 790

12. Which is another way to show 826?

A. $800 + 60 + 2$

B. $80 + 20 + 6$

C. $800 + 20 + 6$

13. What number is modeled?

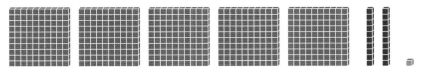

A. 125

B. 521

C. 512

Write the answer.

14. How many hundreds are in 746?

_____

15. How many tens are in 665?

_____

16. How many ones are in 949?

_____

17. How is the value of the 3 different in the numbers 843 and 538?
Explain your answer.

_____

_____

Write the value of the underlined digit.

18. 6<u>2</u>

_____

19. <u>1</u>,000

_____

20. 90<u>7</u>

_____

21. <u>4</u>82

_____

Write the number in expanded form.

22. 691 = _____ hundreds + _____ tens + _____ ones

23. 121 = _____ + _____ + _____

24. 622

_____

25. Write the numbers in order from greatest to least. Use >.

455, 465, 425

26. Write the numbers in order from least to greatest. Use <.

567, 564, 569

Name:

Write how many sides and vertices the plane figure has.

1.

_____ sides   _____ vertices

2.

_____ sides   _____ vertices

3.

_____ sides   _____ vertices

4.

_____ sides   _____ vertices

5.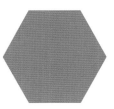

_____ sides   _____ vertices

6.

_____ sides   _____ vertices

T R Y   I T

Write the answer.

7. How many sides does an oval have?

   _____

8. How many vertices does a square have?

   _____

9. Name a shape with 3 vertices.

   _____

Circle the answer.

10. Which shape has more sides, a triangle or a rhombus?

    A. triangle   B. rhombus

11. Which shape has more vertices, a hexagon or a square?

    A. hexagon   B. square

12. Which shape has 4 vertices?

    A. circle   B. oval

    C. triangle   D. rectangle

13. Which shape has 4 sides?

    A. square   B. circle

    C. triangle   D. oval

14. Which shape has no vertices?

    A. square   B. oval

    C. triangle   D. rectangle

TRY IT

Solid Figures

Faces of a Solid

Complete the chart. You may use the blocks.

Solid	Number of Faces of the Shape				Total Number of Faces
	Square	Rectangle	Circle	Triangle	
cube					
rectangular prism					
square pyramid					
cylinder					
cone					
sphere					

LEARN

Faces and Edges of a Solid

Complete the chart. You may use the blocks.

Solid	Shapes of the Faces	Number of Faces	Number of Edges
cube			
rectangular prism			
square pyramid			
cylinder			
cone			
sphere			

Solid Figures
Solids

For Problems 1–24, you may use the blocks.

Write the number of flat faces that the solid has.

1.

_____ faces

2.

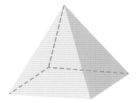

_____ faces

3.

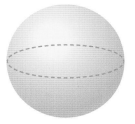

_____ faces

4.

_____ faces

5.

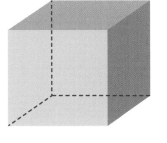

_____ faces

6.

_____ faces

T R Y   I T

Circle the shape of each solid's faces. You may circle more than one shape for each solid.

7.

Solid		Face Shapes		
cylinder	square	rectangle	circle	triangle
rectangular prism	square	rectangle	circle	triangle
cube	square	rectangle	circle	triangle
cone	square	rectangle	circle	triangle

Write the answer.

8. What shapes are the faces of a square pyramid?

_____ and _____

9. What shapes are the faces of a cube?

_____

10. What shapes are the faces of a rectangular prism?

_____ and _____

11. What shape is the face of a cone?

_____

12. What shapes are the faces of a cylinder?

_____

Write the number of edges that the solid has.

13.

_____ edges

14.

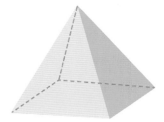

_____ edges

15.

_____ edges

16.

_____ edges

17.

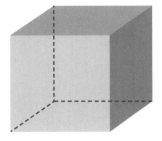

_____ edges

18.

_____ edges

TRY IT

Write the answer.

19. I have 6 faces and 12 edges.
All of my faces are squares.

What solid am I?

_____

20. What solids have curved edges?

_____ and _____

21. What solid has 8 edges?

_____

Circle the answer.

22. Which solid figure has faces that are triangles and a square?

   A. cube   B. sphere

   C. rectangular prism   D. square pyramid

23. Which shape has 6 square faces?

   A. rectangular prism   B. sphere

   C. square pyramid   D. cube

24. Which shape has 2 faces that are circles?

   A. cylinder   B. sphere

   C. rectangular prism   D. cube

TRY IT

Build and Take Apart Shapes

Make and Break Shapes

Put blocks over the shape to show how to make it.
Draw a line or lines on the shape to show how to break it.

1.

Make	Break

211

L E A R N

Draw a line to show how to break the shape into 2 equal parts.

2.

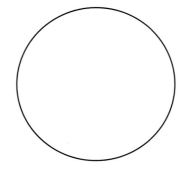

3.

4.

5.

Draw 2 lines to show how to break the shape into 3 shapes.

6.

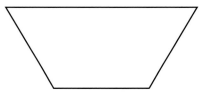

7.

Build and Take Apart Shapes

Hexagon Craze

Use blocks to cover the hexagon to show how to break it.
Then draw lines to show how you broke the hexagon.

1. Use 2 of the same shapes to break the hexagon.

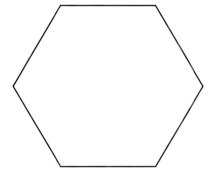

2. Use 3 of the same shapes to break the hexagon.

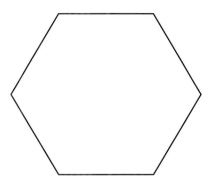

3. Use 6 of the same shapes to break the hexagon.

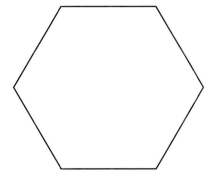

4. Use 3 different shapes to break the hexagon.

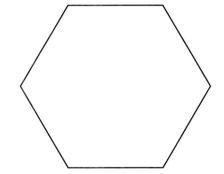

L E A R N

Draw lines to break the hexagon into different shapes.
The shapes do not have to match block shapes.

5.

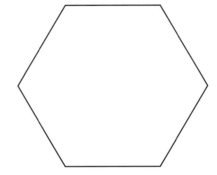

6.

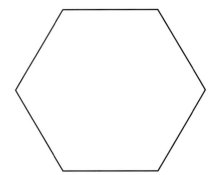

7.

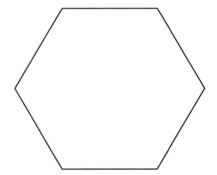

8.

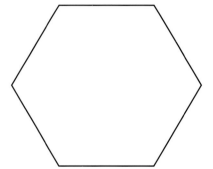

Build and Take Apart Shapes

Construction Zone

Put together the shapes to make a new shape.
Draw the new shape and circle its name.

1.

Shapes	New Shape
	rhombus square
	rectangle trapezoid
	hexagon trapezoid
	rectangle triangle

T R Y   I T

Draw a line or lines to show how to break the shape.

2. Make 3 shapes.

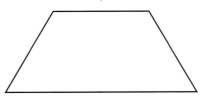

3. Make 2 shapes.

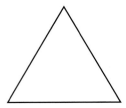

4. Make 2 shapes.

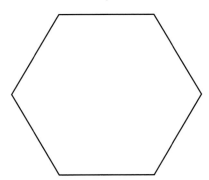

5. Make more than 2 shapes.

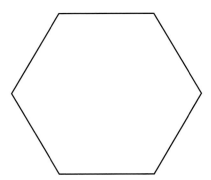

6. Make a triangle and a rhombus.

7. Make 2 triangles.

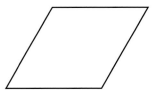

Circle the answer.

8. Which shapes can be combined to make a rhombus?

   A. two triangles   B. a square and a triangle

   C. two trapezoids   D. a rhombus and a square

9. Which shapes can be combined to make a square?

   A. two rectangles   B. a rhombus and a triangle

   C. two squares   D. a triangle and a hexagon

Unit Review

Checkpoint Practice

For Problems 1–20, you may use the blocks.

Write the answer.

1. Name a shape that has 3 sides.

   _____

2. How many vertices does a square have?

   _____ vertices

3. How many vertices does a triangle have?

   _____ vertices

4. How many sides does a rectangle have?

   _____ sides

5. How are these two shapes different?

   _____

   _____

   _____

6. What is the same about these two shapes?

_____

_____

Look at the solid. Write the shapes of its faces. Then write the number of faces it has.

7.

_____ shapes   _____ faces

8.

_____ shapes   _____ faces

9.

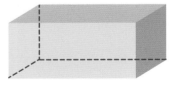

_____ shapes   _____ faces

10.

_____ shapes   _____ faces

UNIT REVIEW

Write the answer.

11. How many edges does a
sphere have?

_____ edges

12. I have 2 faces.
Both of my faces are circles.
What solid am I?

_____

13. What shape is a face of a cube?

_____

Circle the answer.

14. Which shape has 12 edges?

A.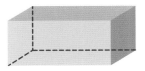

B.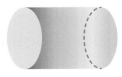

C.

D.

Draw a line or lines to show how to break the shape into
2 or more different shapes.

15.

16.

17.

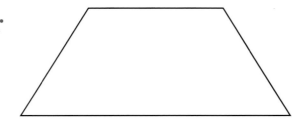

18. Draw a line on the rhombus to form two triangles. (There are two possible answers.)

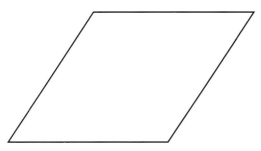 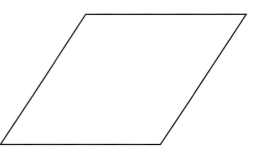

Put together the shapes to make a new shape.
Draw and name the new shape.

19.

_____

20.

_____

Sums and Differences

Find the Sum or Difference

Read the problem and follow the directions.

1. Find the difference. Use base-10 blocks to show the starting number. Then take away blocks to find the difference.

	H Hundreds	T Tens	O Ones
	8	0	4
—	1	9	9

2. Find the sum. Use base-10 blocks to show the addends.

	Th Thousands	,	H Hundreds	T Tens	O Ones
			4	8	6
+			5	1	4

LEARN

3. Find the difference. Use base-10 blocks to show the starting number. Then take away blocks to find the difference.

	Th Thousands	,	H Hundreds	T Tens	O Ones
	1	,	0	0	0
—			3	2	9

4. Find the sum without using base-10 blocks.

517
+ 158
———

5. Find the difference without using base-10 blocks.

1,000
−　297
———

6. Find the difference without using base-10 blocks.

894
− 407
———

L E A R N

Sums and Differences

Practice Adding and Subtracting

Add or subtract. Write the answer.

1.
$$58$$
$$+\ 71$$

2.
$$217$$
$$+\ 452$$

3.
$$486$$
$$+\ 91$$

4.
$$118$$
$$+\ 640$$

5.
$$306$$
$$+\ 306$$

6.
$$715$$
$$+\ 285$$

7.
$$476$$
$$-\ 145$$

8.
$$519$$
$$-\ 57$$

9.
$$711$$
$$-\ 408$$

10.
$$860$$
$$-\ 214$$

11.
$$1{,}000$$
$$-\ 562$$

12.
$$908$$
$$-\ 374$$

TRY IT

Add or subtract. Write the answer.

13.   53
         + 11
         ———

14.   459
         − 278
         ———

Add or subtract. Circle the answer.

15.   821
         + 76
         ———

    A. 897   B. 855
    C. 745   D. 845

16.   634
         − 460
         ———

    A. 234   B. 240
    C. 184   D. 174

Story Problems Through 1,000

Practice Story Problems

Circle Add or Subtract. Then write the correct symbol in the problem on the right and solve.

1. The girls in the nature club collected 347 cans for recycling. The boys in the club collected 534 cans for recycling.

How many cans did both the girls and the boys collect?

Add   Subtract

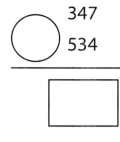

347
534

_____ cans

2. A toy store had 673 toy cars. They sold 425 toy cars.

How many toy cars did the toy store have left?

Add   Subtract

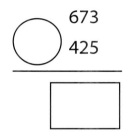

673
425

_____ toy cars

3. Tanya has 675 clear marbles. She has some colored marbles. Tanya has 939 marbles in all.

How many colored marbles does Tanya have?

Add   Subtract

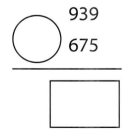

939
675

_____ marbles

TRY IT

4. Brian has 393 baseball cards in a shoebox.

He has 528 cards in his album.

How many baseball cards does Brian have?

Add   Subtract

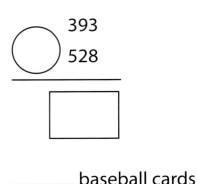

_____ baseball cards

Write the answer.

5. Melia drove to the Grand Canyon. She drove a total of 988 miles in two days. On the first day, Melia drove 455 miles.

How far did Melia drive the second day?
 _____ miles

---

Circle the answer.

6. Mia and Jed are saving up their reward points for a new soccer ball. Mia has saved 332 reward points. Jed has saved 288 reward points.

How many reward points do they have together?

A. 44   B. 156

C. 510   D. 620

7. This year the fundraising committee raised $178. They had already raised $765.

How much money does the committee have now?

A. $587   B. $611

C. $833   D. $943

---

8. Jose drove a total of 420 miles on Saturday and Sunday. He drove 177 miles on Sunday. How many miles did Jose drive on Saturday?

A. 243 miles   B. 353 miles

C. 357 miles   D. 597 miles

TRY IT

Compare and Equalize Problems

Compare Story Problems

Solve.

1. The pet store has 18 birds. The store also has 13 puppies.

   How many more birds than puppies does the pet store have?

   _____ more birds than puppies

2. The pet store has 745 hermit crabs. It has 350 snakes.

   How many fewer snakes than hermit crabs does the pet store have?

   _____ fewer snakes than hermit crabs

3. The pet store has 970 dog bones. It has 495 leashes.

   How many fewer leashes than dog bones does the pet store have?

   _____ fewer leashes than dog bones

   How many more dog bones than leashes does the pet store have?

   _____ more dog bones than leashes

4. The zoo has 700 butterflies. It has 340 birds.

   How many more butterflies are there than birds?

   _____ more butterflies than birds

5. A large seal at the zoo weighs 528 pounds. A small seal weighs 435 pounds.

   How many fewer pounds does the small seal weigh than the large seal?

   _____ fewer pounds

6. The trainer has 849 treats to feed to the animals. There are 1,000 animals. If the trainer gives one treat to each animal, how many animals will **not** get a treat?

   _____ animals will not get a treat

LEARN

Compare and Equalize Problems

More Story Problems

Solve.

1. Jim's stamp collection has 852 stamps. Tina's stamp collection has 614 stamps.

   How many more stamps does Jim have than Tina?

   _____ more stamps

2. Adam has 800 pennies in a blue jar. He has 935 pennies in a red jar.

   How many pennies does he need to put in the blue jar for it to have the same number as the red jar?

   _____ pennies

3. Mac's sticker collection has 546 stickers. Dana's sticker collection has 739 stickers.

   How many fewer stickers does Mac have than Dana?

   _____ fewer stickers

   How many more stickers does Dana have than Mac?

   _____ more stickers

4. A market has 815 apples and 579 bananas.

   How many apples must the market sell to have the same number of apples as bananas?

   _____ apples

   How many more bananas would the market have to get to have the same number of bananas as apples?

   _____ more bananas

5. George has 369 bags of popcorn. Frank has 198 bags of popcorn. How many bags of popcorn does George have to sell to have as many bags as Frank?

   _____ bags

TRY IT

Circle the answer.

6. There is a butterfly house at the zoo. There are 846 monarch butterflies and 574 black swallowtail butterflies.

   There are how many fewer black swallowtails than monarchs?

   A. 72

   B. 272

   C. 332

   D. 372

7. One zoo has 568 animals and another zoo has 388 animals.

   How many more animals does the first zoo have than the second?

   A. 180

   B. 220

   C. 280

   D. 956

8. A large bear weighs 860 pounds. A smaller bear weighs 679 pounds.

   How many pounds would the smaller bear have to gain to weigh the same as the large bear?

   A. 119 pounds

   B. 181 pounds

   C. 219 pounds

   D. 281 pounds

TRY IT

Write Sentences for Story Problems

Practice Setting Up Problems

Write a number sentence for the problem. Then solve.

1. In the first hour, 392 children rode the carousel. In the next hour, 528 children rode it. How many children rode the carousel in the two hours?

_____ children

2. On Friday morning, 384 adults and 532 children rode the rollercoaster. How many more children than adults rode the rollercoaster?

_____ children

3. There were 760 people in line for the log flume. There were 483 people in line for the teacups. How many people need to get in line for the teacups in order for the same number of people to be in each line?

_____ people

4. James won 615 tickets at the arcade. His mom won 164 tickets. How many tickets did they win altogether?

_____ tickets

5. The students in the pottery club made 815 clay pots last year. They painted 622 of the pots. How many pots did **not** get painted?

_____ pots

T R Y   I T

6. Helen sold 444 raffle tickets and Greta sold 123 raffle tickets. How many raffle tickets did they sell altogether?

_____ $\bigcirc$ _____ $\bigcirc$ _____   _____ raffle tickets

---

Circle the answer.

7. Gerald has 942 pennies. Tom has 298 pennies. How many more pennies does Tom need so he has the same number of pennies as Gerald?

   A. $942 + 298 = ?$ B. $942 - 298 = ?$

   C. $298 - 942 = ?$ D. $942 + ? = 298$

8. Elizabeth has 360 songs saved on her computer. Jan has 600 songs saved. How many more songs does Jan have saved than Elizabeth?

   A. $360 + 600 = ?$ B. $600 + ? = 360$

   C. $600 - 360 = ?$ D. $360 - 600 = ?$

9. Mark had 170 beads. He buys 59 more. How many beads does Mark have now?

   A. $170 + 59 = ?$ B. $170 - 59 = ?$

   C. $59 - 170 = ?$ D. $59 + ? = 170$

Find Similarities and Differences

Are They Alike?

Read both story problems. Write the number sentence for each problem. Explain if they can be solved the same way.

1.

There are 468 hardback books in the library. There are 235 paperback books. How many books does the library have?	There are 468 animals in the city zoo. The state zoo has 235 more animals than the city zoo. How many animals does the state zoo have?
_____	_____

Explanation _____

2.

Mrs. Lee bought a box of 510 red beads. Then she bought a box of 350 blue beads. How many beads does she have now?	The club members baked 510 cookies to sell at the bake sale. They sold 350 cookies. How many cookies did they have left after the bake sale?
_____	_____

Explanation _____

LEARN

3.

Brianna has 536 stickers. Rene has 284 stickers. How many more stickers does Brianna have than Rene?	Richard scored 536 points on his computer game. 284 of the points were bonus points. How many points were **not** bonus points?
_____	_____
Explanation _____	

4.

Jonathan has 683 craft sticks. He has 427 short sticks. The rest of the sticks are long. How many craft sticks are long?	Section A of the stadium has 468 people. Section B has 530 people. How many people are in the two sections of the stadium?
_____	_____
Explanation _____	

LEARN

5.

Jack bought some new crayons. The new box has 164 crayons. He already had 500 crayons. How many crayons does Jack have now?

_____

The baseball coach has 425 baseball cards. His son has 391 baseball cards. How many cards do they have altogether?

_____

Explanation _____

6.

The Dragons scored 502 points. The Tigers scored 123 points. How many fewer points did the Tigers score than the Dragons?

_____

Jillian has 756 beads. If she uses 316 beads, then she will have as many beads as Amy. How many beads does Amy have?

_____

Explanation _____

Find Similarities and Differences

Solve the Same Way?

Read both story problems. Write the number sentence for each problem. Explain if they can be solved the same way.

1.

There are 258 students in Lincoln School. There are 419 students in Washington School. How many students are in the two schools?	Lisa has 525 stamps in her collection. Her mother gives her 182 more stamps. How many stamps does Lisa have now?

_____   _____

Explanation _____

2.

A department store had 739 children's watches. They got 481 more watches. How many watches does the store have now?	Brian has 627 tokens in his jar. His sister has 942 tokens in her jar. How many more tokens does Brian's sister have than he does?

_____   _____

Explanation _____

TRY IT

3.

A box of pasta had 860 pieces. Then 182 pieces spilled out. How many pieces are still in the box?	There are 518 children riding rides at the carnival. The rest of the 179 children are walking around. How many children are at the carnival?
_____	_____

Explanation _____

4.

Tiffany won 815 tickets at the carnival before lunch. She played one more game after lunch and won 136 tickets. How many tickets does she have now?	Pedro has 429 marbles. Jennifer has 351 more marbles than Pedro. How many marbles does Jennifer have?
_____	_____

Explanation _____

Circle the answer.

5. Read the complete problem before answering.

Dario walked for 30 minutes in the morning and for 45 minutes in the afternoon. What is the total number of minutes that Dario walked?

A student solved this problem by adding the two numbers. $30 + 45 = ?$

Which of the following problems could be solved the same way?

A. Jason has 26 red balloons. 13 of them popped. How many balloons does Jason have left?

B. Charles baked 53 muffins. He ate 4 of them. How many muffins are left?

C. Emily painted 36 tiles red and 49 tiles orange. How many tiles did Emily paint altogether?

6. Which is the same about these problems?

$700 + 200$

$500 + 300$

A. Both have zeros in the hundreds place.

B. Both have zeros in the tens place only.

C. Both have zeros in the tens and the ones places.

D. Both have a sum of 900.

7. Read the complete problem before answering.

There are 8 carrots on the grass. There are 19 rabbits who want a carrot. If each rabbit tries to get one carrot, how many rabbits will **not** get a carrot?

A student solved this problem by subtracting the two numbers. $19 - 8 = ?$

Which of the following problems could be solved the same way?

A. Tony baked 17 vanilla cupcakes and 15 chocolate cupcakes. How many cupcakes did Tony bake altogether?

B. Hilda is baking pies. She has 8 pie crusts but only has 6 pie dishes. She can only put one pie crust in each dish. How many pie crusts will Hilda have left over?

C. Harry planted some flowers in his yard. He planted 17 roses and 19 tulips. How many flowers did he plant altogether?

8. Read the complete problem before answering.

Joe's Café has 236 seats. Jill's Café has 310 seats. How many fewer seats does Joe's Café have than Jill's?

A student solved this problem by subtracting the two numbers. $310 - 236 = ?$

Which of the following problems could be solved the same way?

A. Lisa rode her bike for 35 minutes. Brooke rode her bike for 45 minutes. How many more minutes did Brooke ride than Lisa?

B. Isabelle has 18 red plums and 15 yellow plums. How many plums does Isabelle have altogether?

C. David had some oranges. He gave 13 oranges away and he has 19 left. How many oranges did David have in the beginning?

Read the problem and follow the directions.

9. Here's a story problem. Write a problem that could be solved in the same way and solve your problem.

   Sally had 216 pennies. Her mom gave her some more and now she has 300 pennies. How many pennies did Sally's mom give her?

   _____

   _____

   _____

   _____

10. Describe how the two problems can be solved in the same way.

    Omar has 15 crayons and buys another 22 crayons. How many crayons does Omar have now?

    Kevin has 98 more marbles than Bernie. Bernie has 20 marbles. How many marbles does Kevin have?

    _____

11. Here's a story problem. Write another story problem that could be solved the same way.

    The clothing store has 65 pairs of jeans and 100 pairs of sweatpants. How many fewer pairs of jeans does the store have than sweatpants?

    _____

    _____

    _____

    _____

TRY IT

Check Story Problem Solutions

Check Answers

Rosa solved these story problems. Solve each problem to check her answers. If Rosa's answer is incorrect, explain what she did wrong.

Story Problem	Rosa's Work	Solve to Check Rosa's Work	Circle Correct or Incorrect. Explain why Rosa's incorrect answers are wrong.
1. The movie theater sold 418 tickets on Saturday and 532 tickets on Sunday. How many tickets did the theater sell for the two days?	$\begin{array}{r} 418 \\ + 532 \\ \hline 950 \end{array}$ The theater sold 950 tickets.	_____ tickets	Correct Incorrect Explain if incorrect: _____ _____
2. Carlos has 874 baseball cards. Derrick has 581 cards. How many more cards does Carlos have than Derrick?	$\begin{array}{r} 874 \\ - 581 \\ \hline 313 \end{array}$ Carlos has 313 more cards.	_____ more cards	Correct Incorrect Explain if incorrect: _____ _____
3. Lenny scored 483 points on the first level of his video game. He scored 301 points on the second level. How many points did he score altogether?	$\begin{array}{r} 483 \\ - 301 \\ \hline 182 \end{array}$ Lenny scored 182 points altogether.	_____ points	Correct Incorrect Explain if incorrect: _____ _____

ADD OR SUBTRACT NUMBERS THROUGH 1,000

243

CHECK STORY PROBLEM SOLUTIONS

Story Problem	Rosa's Work	Solve to Check Rosa's Work	Circle Correct or Incorrect. Explain why Rosa's incorrect answers are wrong.
4. Cindy has 145 swirled marbles. She has 771 solid marbles. How many marbles does she have in all?	$\begin{array}{r} 145 \\ +\,771 \\ \hline 816 \end{array}$ Cindy had 816 marbles in all.	_____ marbles	Correct Incorrect Explain if incorrect: _____ _____
5. There were 963 people at the circus. Then 656 people left the circus. How many people are still at the circus?	$\begin{array}{r} {}^{5\,13}\!\!\!\!\!\!\!\!\! \\ 9\cancel{6}\cancel{3} \\ -\,656 \\ \hline 307 \end{array}$ There are 307 people still at the circus.	_____ people	Correct Incorrect Explain if incorrect: _____ _____
6. Steven has 268 nickels. He has 694 pennies. How many fewer nickels does he have than pennies?	$\begin{array}{r} {}^{1\,1} \\ 268 \\ +\,694 \\ \hline 962 \end{array}$ Steven has 962 fewer nickels.	_____ fewer nickels	Correct Incorrect Explain if incorrect: _____ _____

L E A R N

Check Story Problem Solutions

Practice Checking Answers

Rosa solved these story problems. Solve each problem to check her answers. If Rosa's answer is incorrect, explain what she did wrong.

Story Problem	Rosa's Work	Solve to Check Rosa's Work	Circle Correct or Incorrect. Explain why Rosa's incorrect answers are wrong.
1. There are 762 baseballs on the store shelf. There are 690 bats on display. How many more baseballs are there than bats?	762 $-\,690$ $\overline{132}$ There are 132 more baseballs than bats.	_____ more baseballs	Correct Incorrect Explain if incorrect: _____ _____
2. Sharon has 316 puzzle pieces in the box. She puts in 154 more. How many puzzle pieces are in the box now?	316 $+\,154$ $\overline{460}$ There are 460 puzzle pieces in the box.	_____ pieces	Correct Incorrect Explain if incorrect: _____ _____
3. An art class had 845 craft sticks. Then the students used 380 craft sticks. How many craft sticks are left?	$\overset{7\ \ 14}{\cancel{8}\cancel{4}5}$ $-\,380$ $\overline{465}$ There are 465 craft sticks left.	_____ craft sticks	Correct Incorrect Explain if incorrect: _____ _____

TRY IT

Read the problem and follow the directions.

4. **Rosa solved this story problem.**

    An art gallery has 349 paintings of landscapes. It has 501 paintings of buildings.

    How many paintings does it have altogether?

    Which sentence about Rosa's answer is correct? Circle the answer.

    A. Rosa added and did the math correctly.

    B. Rosa added but made a math mistake.

    C. Rosa should have subtracted.

    Rosa's answer:

    It has 750 paintings altogether.

---

5. **Ron solved this story problem.**

    Gina sold 234 raffle tickets. Toby sold 432 raffle tickets.

    How many more raffle tickets did Toby sell than Gina?

    Write an addition number sentence to check to see if Ron's answer is correct.

    Is Ron correct? _____

    Ron's answer:

    Toby sold 198 more raffle tickets than Gina.

TRY IT

6. **Winnie solved this story problem.**

Adam wrote a story that was 341 words long. He later added some more words to the story and now it has 565 words.

How many words did Adam add to his story?

Write a number sentence to check to see if Winnie's answer is correct.

Is Winnie correct? _____

Winnie's answer:

Adam added 224 words.

---

7. Solve this problem and then check your answer using another way to solve the problem.

The farm store sold 512 eggs the first week. The second week the store sold 88 more eggs than the first week. How many eggs did the store sell the second week?

TRY IT

Explain Operations to Solve

How to Solve Problems

Use a model or sketch to solve the problem and explain your solution.

1. The toy store ordered 573 small marbles. It also ordered 322 large marbles. How many marbles did the toy store order?

_____ marbles

2. The toy store's baby section had 338 bibs and 226 rattles. How many more bibs than rattles were in the baby section?

_____ more bibs than rattles

LEARN

3. Fun Town Toy Store has 429 books. Bozo's Toy Store has 516 books. How many more books does Fun Town need to order to have as many books as Bozo's?

_____ books

4. During its big sale, Bozo's Toy Store had 664 customers. Fun Town Toy Store only had 336 customers during its sale. How many customers shopped at the two stores altogether during the sales?

_____ customers

Explain Operations to Solve

How Would You Solve?

Cut out and fold each strip. Tell how you would solve the problem and explain why. Then turn the strip over to check your answer.

fold

1. Fast Tickets sold 467 tickets online Monday for the concert.
So far today, it has sold 143 tickets online.
How many more tickets does Fast Tickets need to sell online today to equal the number of tickets sold on Monday?

I'm trying to make two amounts equal. I know that 467 is the number I need to reach. I need to find 143 plus "how many more" is 467.

$143 + ? = 467$

I can find the missing number by solving the fact family number sentence $467 - 143 = ?$.

2. An hour before the show, 318 people came in and sat in the top level of seats.
Later 319 more people joined them.
How many people are in the top level?

I know that there were 318 people at the start and that amount changed when 319 more people joined them. Since more people came, I will add.

$318 + 319 = ?$

LEARN

3. Before the start of the concert, the ushers had some programs to sell.
They got 263 more programs to sell later.
They sold all 995 programs.
How many programs did they have at the beginning?

I don't know how many programs the ushers had at the start, but when they got more, I know that the total was 995. Since they got 263 more, I need to add an amount to 263 to make 995.

$? + 263 = 995$

I can find the missing number by solving the fact family number sentence $995 - 263 = ?$.

4. The audience bought 332 candy bars during the show.
They also bought 544 drinks.
How many fewer candy bars did they buy than drinks?

In this problem, I need to compare the number of candy bars to the number of drinks to see how many fewer candy bars people ate.
I need to find the difference, so I will subtract.

$544 - 332 = ?$

5. At the beginning of the concert, there were 945 people.
The music got so loud that 123 people left before the concert ended.
How many people stayed at the concert?

In this problem, 945 people were there at the start. Then 123 people left, so I'll subtract.

$945 - 123 = ?$

LEARN

Explain Operations to Solve

Explain Your Choice

Circle the answer that explains the correct way to solve the problem.

1. Jeff had 280 stamps. Matt had 320 stamps. How many stamps do they have altogether?

   A. Add 280 and 320 because the problem asks for how many stamps altogether.

   B. Subtract 280 from 320 because the problem asks for how many stamps altogether.

2. Jeff had 622 stamps. He bought 15 more stamps. How many stamps does Jeff have now?

   A. Add 622 and 15 because the problem asks about a change in the number of stamps Jeff has after buying 15 more stamps.

   B. Subtract 15 from 622 because the problem asks about a change in the number of stamps Jeff has after buying 15 more stamps.

3. Jeff had 375 stamps. Matt had 324 stamps. How many more stamps does Jeff have than Matt?

   A. Add 375 and 324 because the problem asks how many more stamps Matt has than Jeff.

   B. Subtract 324 from 375 because the problem asks how many more stamps Jeff has then Matt.

4. Jeff had 535 stamps. Matt had 633 stamps. How many stamps does Jeff need to buy to have as many stamps as Matt?

   A. Add 535 and 633 because the problem asks how many stamps Jeff needs to have the same number as Matt.

   B. Subtract 535 from 633 because the problem asks how many stamps Jeff needs to have the same number as Matt.

TRY IT

5. Explain how to solve this problem.

Manny had 603 nails before he started to build a doghouse. When he finished he had 7 nails left. How many nails did Manny use to build the doghouse?

A. $603 - 7 = ?$ because Manny now has more nails than when he started.

B. $603 - 7 = ?$ because Manny now has fewer nails than when he started.

C. $603 + 7 = ?$ because Manny now has more nails than when he started.

---

6. Explain how to solve this problem.

Tommy had 1,000 peanuts. He gave some to his friends. He now has 899 peanuts left. How many peanuts did Tommy give to his friends?

A. Add 1,000 and 899 because Tommy now has more peanuts than he started with.

B. Subtract 899 from 1,000 because Tommy now has more peanuts than he started with.

C. Subtract 899 from 1,000 because Tommy now has fewer peanuts than he started with.

7. Explain how to solve this problem.

There were 23 dogs at the dog park. Someone brought
15 balls for the dogs to play with. If each dog was given 1 ball,
how many dogs did **not** get a ball to play with?

A. $23 + 15 = ?$ because there are lots of dogs and balls.

B. $23 - 15 = ?$ because all of the dogs won't get a ball.

C. $15 - 23 = ?$ because all of the dogs won't get a ball.

---

8. Read this problem.

There were 550 people in the park.
120 people left the park when it started to rain.
How many people are in the park now?

Which number sentence could be used to solve this problem? Why?

A. $550 + 120 = ?$
There will be more people in the park after it starts to rain.

B. $550 - 120 = ?$
There will be fewer people in the park after it starts to rain.

C. $120 - 550 = ?$
There will be fewer people in the park after it starts to rain.

TRY IT

Choose the Problem

Add or Subtract?

Circle the problem that would most easily be solved by addition.

1.

There are 658 children signed up for summer camp. Of that group, 274 of them will go to overnight camp. How many will **not** go to overnight camp?

Carrie's garden has 539 flowers. If she plants another 280 flowers, her garden will have the same number of flowers as Lori's garden. How many flowers are in Lori's garden?

2.

A butterfly garden has 295 blue butterflies and 481 golden butterflies. How many butterflies does the garden have?

A zoo has 819 animals. The zookeeper has fed 482 of the animals. How many more animals does the zookeeper need to feed?

Circle the problem that would most easily be solved by subtraction.

3.

There are 758 blue beads in the craft box. There are 592 orange beads in the craft box. How many more orange beads are needed to have the same number of orange beads as blue beads?

There were 603 people at the carnival. Then 387 people arrived at the carnival. How many people are at the carnival now?

4.

There were 429 cars in the parking lot. Then 144 cars left. How many cars are still in the parking lot?

There were 583 riders on the Ferris wheel today. Yesterday there were 245 riders. How many riders were on the Ferris wheel on both days?

L E A R N

Circle the problem that would most easily be solved by addition.

5.

| Anita has 593 stickers. She gets another 243 stickers. How many stickers does she have now? | A large bookcase has 850 books. A smaller bookcase has 480 books. How many more books does the larger bookcase have? |

6.

| A party room had 420 balloons. Children took 106 balloons home. How many balloons are still in the party room? | Peter has 582 baseball cards. Audrey has 208 more cards than Peter. How many cards does Audrey have? |

Circle the problem that would most easily be solved by subtraction.

7.

| A toy store has 740 games. The store orders another 294 games. How many games will the store have? | A sports museum has pictures of 840 baseball players. It has 938 pictures of football players. How many fewer baseball player pictures does it have? |

8.

| Casey bought a stamp book with 307 stamps. She already has a stamp book with 563 stamps. How many stamps does she have now? | There were 631 bundles of newspaper at the recycling plant. Then a delivery truck brought 402 bundles of cardboard. How many more bundles of cardboard need to be delivered so that there are the same number of cardboard bundles as newspaper bundles? |

LEARN

Choose the Problem

Choose the Operation

Circle the problem that would most easily be solved by addition.

1.

| The pet store had 593 fish. The store sold 304 fish. How many fish are in the store now? | There were 492 small dogs at the dog show. There were 309 large dogs at the show. How many large and small dogs were at the show? |

2.

| There are 739 children and 402 adults at the park. How many more children than adults are there? | A farm has 482 chickens. If they received another 119 chickens, they would have the same number of chickens as cows. How many cows does the farm have? |

Circle the problem that would most easily be solved by subtraction.

3.

| There are 830 puzzle pieces in a box. There are 493 puzzle pieces in a bag. How many fewer puzzle pieces are in the bag than the box? | A container has 510 snap beads. Maria puts in another 394 snap beads. How many snap beads are in the container now? |

4.

| Ravi has 492 marbles in his jar. Karen has 112 more marbles than Ravi. How many marbles does Karen have? | There are 632 people watching a girls' soccer game. There are 540 people watching a boys' soccer game. How many more people need to watch the boys' game so that there are the same number of people watching both games? |

TRY IT

Circle the answer.

5. Can this problem be solved by adding the two numbers in the problem?

   Joe has 527 pennies. Jen has 208 pennies. How many pennies do they have altogether?

   A. Yes   B. No

---

6. Which problem could be solved by subtracting one number in the problem from the other?

   A. Zen ran 750 yards. She then ran 250 more yards. How far did she run?

   B. Anne had 540 pennies. She gave her mother 175 pennies. How many pennies does Anne have left?

   C. Tom ran 350 yards on Monday and 500 yards on Tuesday. How many yards did Tom run in all?

   D. Anne had 546 pennies. Her mother gave her 175 more pennies. How many pennies does Anne have now?

---

7. Which expression could be used to solve this problem?

   A shelf in a music store will hold 600 CDs. There are 152 CDs on the shelf now. How many more CDs can be put on the shelf?

   A. $600 + 152$

   B. $600 - 152$

   C. $152 - 600$

---

8. Can this problem be solved by subtracting one number in the problem from the other?

   There were 409 children at the carnival. 102 more children arrived. How many children are at the carnival now?

   A. Yes   B. No

TRY IT

Unit Review

Checkpoint Practice

Solve the problem. Use the blank space to show your work.

1. Roz has 629 yellow beads.
   She has 149 orange beads.

   How many yellow and orange
   beads does Roz have?

   _____ beads

2. There are 843 napkins in a
   package. The Smith family uses
   284 napkins at a reunion.

   How many napkins are left in
   the package?

   _____ napkins

Write a number sentence that could be used to solve each problem, and then solve. Use the blank space to show your work.

3. Ty has 893 rocks in his collection.
   He has 557 labels.

   If he puts one label on each rock
   how many rocks will **not** get a label?

   _____ rocks

4. A park ranger buys 428 flyers.
   There are 625 visitors.

   How many more flyers will the
   ranger need to get to have the same
   number as visitors?

   _____ flyers

Read both story problems. Explain how they can be solved the same way. Say your answer.

5.

| There are 371 children in Oak Park. There are 529 children in Maple Park. How many children are in the two parks? | There are 371 stickers in Grace's collection. Her mother gives her 529 more stickers. How many stickers does she have now? |

6.

| A store has 394 baseball caps on display. They sell 194 baseball caps. How many baseball caps do they have now? | Jack has 743 pennies in his jar. His sister has 820 pennies in her jar. How many more pennies does Jack's sister have than he does? |

Rosa solved these story problems. Solve each problem to check her answers. Write Correct or Incorrect. If Rosa's answer is incorrect, explain what she did wrong.

Story Problem	Rosa's Answer	Solve and Check	Correct or Incorrect?
7. There are 830 trucks on the store shelf. There are 750 cars on display. How many more trucks are there than cars?	There are 120 more trucks than cars.		_____ _____ _____
8. An art class had 647 crayons. The students used 380 crayons. How many crayons were not used?	267 crayons were not used.		_____ _____

Read both problems. If you would use addition to solve the problem, circle the problem. If you would use subtraction to solve, underline the problem.

9.

Will has 593 cards in his collection. Jan has 102 more cards than Will. How many cards does Jan have?

There are 830 seats at the show. 305 people came to watch the show. How many more people need to come to fill all the seats?

Circle the answer.

10.

$$724$$
$$-\ 275$$

A. 449   B. 549

C. 551   D. 559

11. An elephant ate 300 kg of leaves and grass in a day. The elephant ate 178 kg of leaves. How much grass did it eat?

A. 122 kg   B. 232 kg

C. 278 kg   D. 478 kg

12. Which problem could be solved by subtracting one number in the problem from the other?

A. Rachel had some money. She gave $5 away to her sister and now she has $26 left. How much money did she have in the beginning?

B. A farmer had 118 bales of hay. He fed 59 bales to his horses over the winter. How many bales does he have now?

C. Harry rode his bike 18 times around the track in the morning and 9 times in the afternoon. How many times did he ride around the track in all?

13. Adam and Coleen ordered peach slices with their lunches. Adam got 34 peach slices. He got 16 fewer than Coleen. How many peach slices did Coleen get?

A. 18   B. 28   C. 40   D. 50

Read the problem and follow the directions.

14. Lixia's family is driving to their family reunion. They drove part of the way in the morning and 432 miles in the afternoon. They drove a total of 576 miles.

   How many miles did Lixia's family drive in the morning? _____ miles

15. Gustav has 212 pennies. If he gets 12 more, he will have the same number of pennies as Chris. How many pennies does Chris have?

   _____ pennies

16. Write a number sentence that could be used to solve this problem, and then solve it.

   Skyler's turtle walked 28 inches to his water dish and then walked another 12 inches to the grass. How many inches did the turtle walk altogether?

    _____ inches

17. Read the story problem. Then write a problem that could be solved in the same way and solve your problem.

   On Sunday it took the firefighters 59 minutes to clean their fire truck. On Monday it took them 45 minutes. How many fewer minutes did it take them to clean the truck on Monday than on Sunday?

   _____

   _____

   _____

18. Solve this problem, and then check your answer using another way to solve the problem.

Alan painted 79 feet of fence on Sunday and another 21 feet of fence on Monday. How many feet of fence did Alan paint altogether?

_____ feet

19. Solve this problem, and then explain why you solved it the way you did.

Eliza had 9 oranges in one basket and 17 oranges in another basket. How many oranges did Eliza have altogether?

_____ oranges

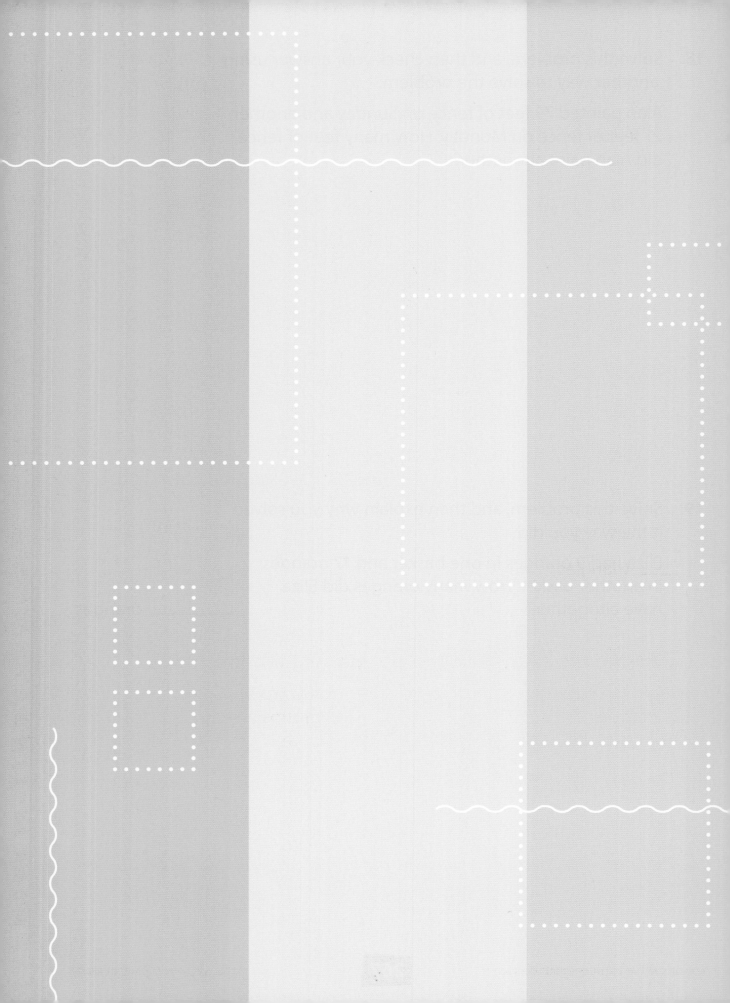

Model Multiplication with Arrays

Label and Draw Arrays

Fill in the blanks to describe the array.

1.

2.

3.

_____ rows of _____	_____ rows of _____	_____ row of _____
_____ groups of _____	_____ groups of _____	_____ group of _____
_____ times _____	_____ times _____	_____ times _____
_____ triangles altogether	_____ flowers altogether	_____ stars altogether

Draw the array. You may draw dots or circles, or use grid paper.

4. 2 rows of 10
2 groups of 10
2 times 10

5. 5 rows of 4
5 groups of 4
5 times 4

T R Y   I T

Circle the answer.

6. Which array shows 3 times 6?

A.

B.

C.

D.

Use circles to make the array. You may use grid paper. Then count the circles to complete the multiplication sentence.

7. 4 times 3

   4 times 3 is _____

8. 3 times 6

   3 times 6 is _____

9. 2 times 4

   2 times 4 is _____

T R Y   I T

Repeated Addition and Grouping

Repeated Addition

Use cubes to show the array in the grid. On the line next to each row of cubes, write how many cubes are in the row. Then write the repeated addition sentence that shows how many cubes there are altogether.

1. 3 times 5

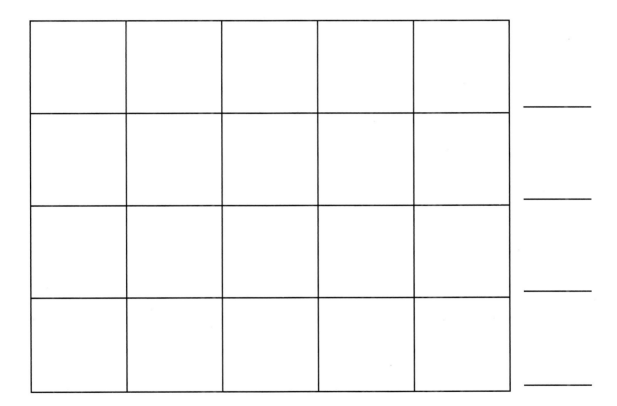

Repeated addition sentence:

_____ + _____ + _____ = _____

LEARN

2. 4 times 2

Repeated addition sentence:

_____ + _____ + _____ + _____ = _____

3. 3 times 4

Repeated addition sentence:

_____ + _____ + _____ = _____

LEARN

Draw an array to show the problem. At the end of each row, write how many sketches are in the row. Then write a repeated addition sentence and solve the problem.

4. Mandy planted flowers in an array.
   She made 3 rows.
   She planted 10 flowers in each row.
   How many flowers did Mandy plant in all?

Repeated addition sentence:

_____ + _____ + _____ = _____

_____ flowers

Repeated Addition and Grouping

Use Groups to Multiply

An array and groups are two ways to show the same problem. Use either or both models to solve the problem. Write the answer.

1. 2 times 5 equals _____

 5
 5

 5    5

2. 7 times 2 equals _____

 2
 2
 2
 2
 2
2
2

 2    2

 2   2

2   2   2

Use the models of equal groups to solve the problem. You may skip count. Write the answer.

3. 6 times 2 equals _____

 2
 2
 2
 2
 2
 2

L E A R N

4. 4 times 5 equals _____

 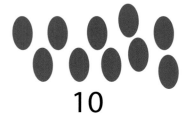 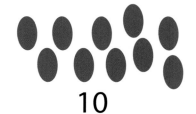 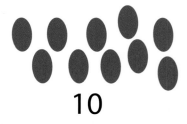

     5   5   5   5

5. 3 times 10 equals _____

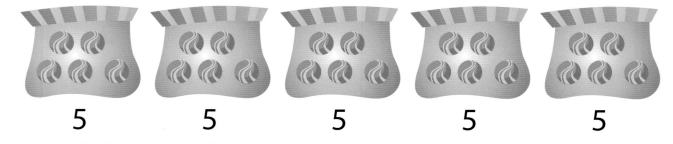

     10   10   10

Solve using any method you choose.

6. 5 children were playing marbles. Each child had 5 marbles. How many marbles do the children have altogether?

_____ marbles

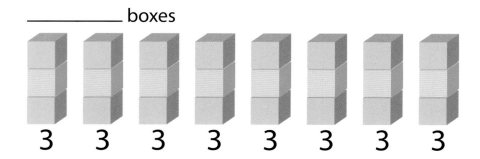

   5   5   5   5   5

7. The store has 8 stacks of boxes. Each stack has 3 boxes. How many boxes are there in all the stacks?

_____ boxes

  3   3   3   3   3   3   3   3

Repeated Addition and Grouping
Model and Multiply

For Problems 3–7, use cubes.
Write a repeated addition sentence to solve the problem.
Then write the answer.

1. 8 times 5 equals ?

8 times 5 is _____

2. 2 times 10 equals ?

_____

2 times 10 is _____

Read the problem and follow the directions.

3. Build 3 groups of 5 with your cubes. Show that skip counting to find the total of 3 groups of 5 gives the same answer as adding 5 three times.

---

4. Make an array with your cubes to show that 5 times 2 means the same as $2 + 2 + 2 + 2 + 2$.

Make groups of cubes to model the problem. Skip count to solve. Then write the answer.

5. 8 times 2 is

_____

6. 6 times 5 is

_____

7. 7 times 5 is

_____

TRY IT

Read the problem and follow the directions.

8. Draw an array to show the problem. Write a repeated addition sentence to solve the problem. Then write the answer.

There are 6 rows of chairs.
Each row has 10 chairs in it.
How many chairs are there in all?

_____

6 times 10 equals _____   _____ chairs

9. Draw a picture using groups to solve the problem.
Then write the answer.

Diane collects buttons.
She arranged her buttons in an array of 6 rows of 5 buttons.
She wants to put her buttons into bags.
Each bag will have 5 buttons.
How many bags does Diane need?   _____ bags

10. Use any method to solve the problem. Then write the answer.

There are 9 strings of beads.
There are 10 beads on each string.
How many beads are there in all?   _____ beads

Circle the answer. You may make a sketch.

11. Carl has 6 groups of 5 balls. How many balls does he have altogether?

A. 5   B. 6   C. 11   D. 30

12. Valerie sees 4 groups of 10 ants. How many ants does she see altogether?

A. 40   B. 14   C. 10   D. 4

TRY IT

Model and Solve Multiplication

Model to Multiply

Draw an array with circles to model the problem. Write the repeated addition sentence that shows how many circles there are altogether. Then complete the multiplication sentence.

1. 2 times 7

Repeated addition sentence: _____

2 times 7 equals _____

2. 4 times 4

Repeated addition sentence: _____

4 times 4 equals _____

TRY IT

Draw groups of circles to model the problem. Skip count to find the answer. Then complete the multiplication sentence.

3. 3 times 10

3 times 10 equals _____

4. 4 times 5

4 times 5 equals _____

Use circles to model the problem. You may model the problem with an array or a group model. Then complete the multiplication sentence and answer the problem.

5. There are 2 trays of glasses with 5 glasses on each tray.

How many glasses are there in all?

_____ times _____ equals _____

_____ glasses

6. Kelly puts 5 rows of muffins in a box.
She puts 4 muffins in each row.

How many muffins are there in the box altogether?

_____ times _____ equals _____

_____ muffins

7. There are 6 baskets of flowers.
There are 5 flowers in each basket.

How many flowers are there in all?

_____ times _____ equals _____

_____ flowers

8. There are 2 packages of juice boxes.
There are 10 juice boxes on each package.

How many juice boxes are there in all?

_____ times _____ equals _____

_____ juice boxes

Circle the answer.

9. Which array shows 4 times 5?

A.

B.

C.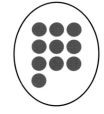

D.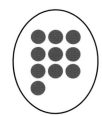

10. Which sketch shows that 5 times 5 means $5 + 5 + 5 + 5 + 5$?

A.

B.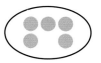

C.

D.

T R Y   I T

11. Which groups of dots show the following multiplication problem?

$6 \times 5 =$ _____

A.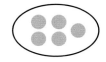

B.

C.

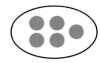

D.

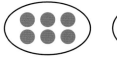

TRY IT

Linear Patterns

Pattern Rules and What's Next

Read the problem and follow the directions.

1. A nickel is worth 5 cents. The table shows the pattern.

   What is the rule that describes the pattern?

Rule: times _____				
Number of nickels	1	2	3	4
Number of cents	5	10	15	?

   Continue the pattern.

   How many cents are 4 nickels worth? _____

2. Gabby has 4 sheets of stickers. Each sheet has 10 stickers. The table shows the pattern.

   What is the rule that describes the pattern?

Rule: times _____						
Number of sheets	1	2	3	4	5	6
Number of stickers	10	20	30	40	?	?

   Continue the pattern.

   How many stickers are there on 5 sheets? _____

   How many stickers are there on 6 sheets? _____

TRY IT

Circle the answer. You may draw a table.

3. There were 4 ducks on the pond.
   1 duck has 2 legs.
   2 ducks have a total of 4 legs.
   3 ducks have a total of 6 legs.
   4 ducks have a total of 8 legs.

   Which rule describes this pattern?

   A. times 2   B. times 4   C. add 1   D. add 8

4. There are strawberry plants in the garden.
   1 strawberry plant has 5 strawberries.
   2 strawberry plants have 10 strawberries.
   3 strawberry plants have 15 strawberries.
   4 strawberry plants have 20 strawberries.

   Which rule describes this pattern?

   A. add 1   B. add 4   C. times 5   D. times 10

5. Lori's aunt is a running coach. She is keeping track of how
   many miles she runs in a week.
   After 1 day, she had run 3 miles.
   After 2 days, she had run 6 miles.
   After 3 days, she had run 9 miles.
   After 4 days, she had run 12 miles.

   If she continues the same pattern, how many miles will she
   have run after 5 days?

   A. 8   B. 14   C. 15   D. 16

TRY IT

Read the problem and follow the directions.

6. The bike store has 4 new bikes.
   1 bicycle has 2 wheels.
   2 bicycles have 4 wheels.
   3 bicycles have 6 wheels.
   4 bicycles have 8 wheels.

   The rule for this pattern is times _____.

7. Katherine picked flowers every day.

   What is the rule that describes the pattern?

Rule: add _____				
Day	1	2	3	4
Flowers picked	3	4	5	?

   Continue the pattern.

   How many flowers did Katherine pick on day 4? _____

Number Patterns

What's Missing?

Read the problem and follow the directions.

1. Corey is arranging his rock collection into groups with 5 rocks in each pile.
   1 group has 5 rocks.
   2 groups have a total of 10 rocks.
   3 groups have a total of 15 rocks.

   Corey has 6 groups of rocks. How many rocks does Corey have? Circle the answwer.

   A. 26   B. 27

   C. 28   D. 30

Corey's Rocks	
Number of groups	Number of rocks
1	5
2	10
3	15
4	20
5	25
6	?

2. Carly is handing out tennis balls for the students in the tennis class.
   Each student will be given 2 tennis balls.
   If there is 1 student, Carly will need 2 tennis balls.
   If there are 2 students, Carly will need 4 tennis balls.
   If there are 3 students, Carly will need 6 tennis balls.

   How many tennis balls will Carly need if there are 7 students?

   _____ tennis balls

Tennis Balls	
Number of students	Number of tennis balls
1	2
2	4
3	6
4	?
5	?
6	?
7	?

3. Lina is putting her pictures into her photo album.
She puts 5 photos on each page.
Lina noticed that if she uses 1 page, she has a total of 5 photos.
If she uses 2 pages, she has a total of 10 photos.
If she uses 3 pages, she has a total of 15 photos.

How many photos does Lina have if she uses 9 pages?

_____ photos

Lina's Photos	
Number of pages	Number of photos
1	5
2	10
3	15
4	20
5	25
6	30
7	35
8	40
9	?

4. Mrs. Walker is making the skirts for the ballet students.
Each skirt needs 10 ribbons.
If she makes 1 skirt, she needs 10 ribbons.
If she makes 2 skirts, she needs 20 ribbons.
If she makes 3 skirts, she needs 30 ribbons.

How many ribbons will Mrs. Walker need to make 8 skirts? Circle the answer.

A. 70   B. 80

C. 90   D. 100

Ballet Skirts	
Number of students	Number of ribbons
1	10
2	20
3	30
4	40
5	50
6	60
7	?
8	?

TRY IT

5. Wally is putting dimes in his empty piggy bank.
A dime is worth 10 cents.
The chart shows the number of dimes Wally puts in his bank.

How many cents are 6 dimes?

_____ cents

Dimes	
Number of dimes	Amount of money in cents
1	10
2	20
3	30
4	40
5	?
6	?

Circle the number that comes next in the pattern.

6. 4, 6, 8, 10, 12, _____

    A. 12   B. 13   C. 14   D. 16

7. 20, 30, 40, 50, 60, _____

    A. 40   B. 60   C. 65   D. 70

8. 15, 20, 25, 30, 35, _____

    A. 40   B. 45   C. 50   D. 56

Fill in the missing number in the pattern.

9. 6, 8, 10, 12, 14, _____, 18

Represent Multiplication
Multiplication Sentences

Draw a picture to match the multiplication sentence.

1. $2 \times 6 = 12$

2. $3 \times 3 = 9$

3. $7 \times 3 = 21$

4. $2 \times 5 = 10$

TRY IT

Write a multiplication sentence to match the picture.

5.

_____

6.

_____

7.

_____

8.

_____

TRY IT

Write a multiplication sentence to match the words.

9. 3 groups of 4 people is 12 people. _____

10. 18 is 9 rows of 2. _____

Read the problem and follow the directions.

11. Use the ones cubes to model the problem.

$3 \times 5 =$ _____

12. Write a multiplication sentence for the model.

_____

13. What does this symbol mean? Say the answer.

$$3 \times 4 = 12$$
$$\uparrow$$

---

14. Which symbol goes in the box to make the number sentence true? Circle the answer.

5 ☐ 2 = 5 groups of 2

A. $+$

B. $-$

C. $\times$

D. $\div$

Multiply by 2

Practice Multiplying by 2

Write the answer.

1. $3 \times 2 = $ _____

2. $1 \times 2 = $ _____

3. $4 \times 2 = $ _____

4. $9 \times 2 = $ _____

5.
$$\begin{array}{r} 10 \\ \times\ 2 \\ \hline \end{array}$$

6.
$$\begin{array}{r} 7 \\ \times\ 2 \\ \hline \end{array}$$

7.
$$\begin{array}{r} 6 \\ \times\ 2 \\ \hline \end{array}$$

8.
$$\begin{array}{r} 2 \\ \times\ 2 \\ \hline \end{array}$$

9.
$$\begin{array}{r} 8 \\ \times\ 2 \\ \hline \end{array}$$

10.
$$\begin{array}{r} 5 \\ \times\ 2 \\ \hline \end{array}$$

TRY IT

11. $\begin{array}{r} 1 \\ \times\ 2 \\ \hline \end{array}$

12. $\begin{array}{r} 9 \\ \times\ 2 \\ \hline \end{array}$

13. $\begin{array}{r} 4 \\ \times\ 2 \\ \hline \end{array}$

14. $\begin{array}{r} 3 \\ \times\ 2 \\ \hline \end{array}$

15. $2 \times 2 =$ _____

16. $5 \times 2 =$ _____

17. $7 \times 2 =$ _____

Multiplication: 2s Facts

Practice the 2s Facts

Write the answer without using a model.

1. $9 \times 2 =$ _____

2. $2 \times 2 =$ _____

3. $5 \times 2 =$ _____

4. $7 \times 2 =$ _____

5. $10 \times 2 =$ _____

6. $1 \times 2 =$ _____

7.
$$\begin{array}{r} 5 \\ \times\ 2 \\ \hline \end{array}$$

8.
$$\begin{array}{r} 2 \\ \times\ 2 \\ \hline \end{array}$$

9.
$$\begin{array}{r} 1 \\ \times\ 2 \\ \hline \end{array}$$

10.
$$\begin{array}{r} 3 \\ \times\ 2 \\ \hline \end{array}$$

T R Y   I T

11. $4 \times 2 =$ _____

12. $8 \times 2 =$ _____

13. $6 \times 2 =$ _____

14. $3 \times 2 =$ _____

15.
$$\begin{array}{r} 8 \\ \times\ 2 \\ \hline \end{array}$$

16.
$$\begin{array}{r} 6 \\ \times\ 2 \\ \hline \end{array}$$

17.
$$\begin{array}{r} 4 \\ \times\ 2 \\ \hline \end{array}$$

18.
$$\begin{array}{r} 9 \\ \times\ 2 \\ \hline \end{array}$$

19.
$$\begin{array}{r} 7 \\ \times\ 2 \\ \hline \end{array}$$

20.
$$\begin{array}{r} 10 \\ \times\ 2 \\ \hline \end{array}$$

TRY IT

Multiply by 10

Practice Multiplying by 10

Write the answer.

1. $9 \times 10 = $ _____

2. $1 \times 10 = $ _____

3. $10 \times 10 = $ _____

4. $4 \times 10 = $ _____

5. $3 \times 10 = $ _____

6. $5 \times 10 = $ _____

7. $6 \times 10 = $ _____

8. $2 \times 10 = $ _____

9. $8 \times 10 = $ _____

10. $7 \times 10 = $ _____

T R Y   I T

11. $\begin{array}{r} 10 \\ \times\ 10 \\ \hline \end{array}$

12. $\begin{array}{r} 9 \\ \times\ 10 \\ \hline \end{array}$

13. $\begin{array}{r} 2 \\ \times\ 10 \\ \hline \end{array}$

14. $\begin{array}{r} 6 \\ \times\ 10 \\ \hline \end{array}$

15. $\begin{array}{r} 5 \\ \times\ 10 \\ \hline \end{array}$

16. $\begin{array}{r} 7 \\ \times\ 10 \\ \hline \end{array}$

17. $\begin{array}{r} 3 \\ \times\ 10 \\ \hline \end{array}$

18. $\begin{array}{r} 8 \\ \times\ 10 \\ \hline \end{array}$

Solve.

19. Count by 10s to find the answer to 10×10.

_____

Multiplication: 10s Facts

Practice the 10s Facts

Write the answer without using a model.

1. $9 \times 10 =$ _____

2. $10 \times 10 =$ _____

3. $5 \times 10 =$ _____

4. $7 \times 10 =$ _____

5. $2 \times 10 =$ _____

6. $1 \times 10 =$ _____

7. $4 \times 10 =$ _____

8. $8 \times 10 =$ _____

9. $3 \times 10 =$ _____

10. $6 \times 10 =$ _____

TRY IT

11.   3
      × 10

12.   8
      × 10

13.   6
      × 10

14.   4
      × 10

15.   9
      × 10

16.   7
      × 10

17.   5
      × 10

18.   2
      × 10

19.   1
      × 10

20.   10
      × 10

TRY IT

Multiply by 5

Practice Multiplying by 5

Write the answer.

1. $9 \times 5 =$ _____

2. $1 \times 5 =$ _____

3. $5 \times 5 =$ _____

4. $4 \times 5 =$ _____

5. $3 \times 5 =$ _____

6. $2 \times 5 =$ _____

7. $6 \times 5 =$ _____

8. $10 \times 5 =$ _____

9. $8 \times 5 =$ _____

10. $7 \times 5 =$ _____

TRY IT

11. $\begin{array}{r} 5 \\ \times\ 5 \\ \hline \end{array}$	**12.** $\begin{array}{r} 9 \\ \times\ 5 \\ \hline \end{array}$
13. $\begin{array}{r} 10 \\ \times\ 5 \\ \hline \end{array}$	**14.** $\begin{array}{r} 6 \\ \times\ 5 \\ \hline \end{array}$
15. $\begin{array}{r} 2 \\ \times\ 5 \\ \hline \end{array}$	**16.** $\begin{array}{r} 7 \\ \times\ 5 \\ \hline \end{array}$
17. $\begin{array}{r} 3 \\ \times\ 5 \\ \hline \end{array}$	**18.** $\begin{array}{r} 8 \\ \times\ 5 \\ \hline \end{array}$

Solve.

19. Count by 5s to find the answer to 10×5.

_____

TRY IT

Multiplication: 5s Facts

Practice the 5s Facts

Write the answer without using a model.

1. $9 \times 5 =$ _____

2. $10 \times 5 =$ _____

3. $5 \times 5 =$ _____

4. $7 \times 5 =$ _____

5. $2 \times 5 =$ _____

6. $1 \times 5 =$ _____

7.
$$\begin{array}{r} 3 \\ \times\ 5 \\ \hline \end{array}$$

8.
$$\begin{array}{r} 8 \\ \times\ 5 \\ \hline \end{array}$$

9.
$$\begin{array}{r} 6 \\ \times\ 5 \\ \hline \end{array}$$

10.
$$\begin{array}{r} 4 \\ \times\ 5 \\ \hline \end{array}$$

TRY IT

11. $4 \times 5 =$ _____

12. $8 \times 5 =$ _____

13. $6 \times 5 =$ _____

14. $3 \times 5 =$ _____

15. $1 \times 5 =$ _____

16. $5 \times 5 =$ _____

17.
$$\begin{array}{r} 9 \\ \times\, 5 \\ \hline \end{array}$$

18.
$$\begin{array}{r} 7 \\ \times\, 5 \\ \hline \end{array}$$

19.
$$\begin{array}{r} 10 \\ \times\, 5 \\ \hline \end{array}$$

20.
$$\begin{array}{r} 2 \\ \times\, 5 \\ \hline \end{array}$$

Unit Review

Checkpoint Practice

Complete the sentence for the array.

1.

   _____ rows of _____

2.  _____ rows of _____

Draw an array or a picture to show the problem. Write the addition sentence you can use to solve the problem. Then solve the problem.

3. There are 4 boxes of cups with 8 cups in each box.

   How many cups are there in all?

   _____   _____ cups

4. Tammy put chairs in 6 rows with 5 chairs in each row.

How many chairs are there in all?

_____   _____ chairs

Read the problem and follow the directions.

5. Jessie uses 10 beads to make each bracelet.
The table shows the pattern.

Rule: times _____				
Number of bracelets	1	2	3	4
Number of beads	10	20	30	?

Continue the pattern.

How many beads does Jessie use for 4 bracelets?   _____

6. Write the number that comes next in the pattern.

10, 20, 30, 40, 50, _____

7. What number is missing in the pattern?

30, 35, 40, 45, _____, 55

Circle the answer.

8. Corey is arranging his rock collection into groups with 5 rocks in each pile.
1 group has 5 rocks.
2 groups have a total of 10 rocks.
3 groups have a total of 15 rocks.

Corey has 6 groups of rocks. How many rocks does Corey have?

A. 26   B. 27

C. 28   D. 30

Corey's Rocks	
Number of groups	Number of rocks
1	5
2	10
3	15
4	20
5	25
6	?

9. Count by 10s to find the answer to 2 × 10.

A. 18   B. 20   C. 30   D. 40

10. Which shows 4 × 2?

A.

B.

C.

D.

11. Circle the symbol that means "to multiply."

A. =   B. +   C. −   D. ×

12. Steve recycles plastic bottles each week.
After 1 week, he had recycled 10 plastic bottles.
After 2 weeks, he had recycled a total of 20 plastic bottles.
After 3 weeks, he had recycled a total of 30 plastic bottles.

If this pattern continued, how many plastic bottles would Steve have recycled after 4 weeks?

A. 25   B. 50   C. 45   D. 40

Solve.

13. $6 \times 2 = $ _____

14. $3 \times 10 = $ _____

15. $4 \times 5 = $ _____

16. $8 \times 2 = $ _____

17. $\begin{array}{r} 7 \\ \times\ 10 \\ \hline \end{array}$

18. $\begin{array}{r} 9 \\ \times\ 2 \\ \hline \end{array}$

19. $\begin{array}{r} 3 \\ \times\ 5 \\ \hline \end{array}$

20. $\begin{array}{r} 2 \\ \times\ 5 \\ \hline \end{array}$

21. $\begin{array}{r} 1 \\ \times\ 10 \\ \hline \end{array}$

22. $\begin{array}{r} 8 \\ \times\ 5 \\ \hline \end{array}$

23. $9 \times 10 = $ _____

24. $\begin{array}{r} 7 \\ \times\ 2 \\ \hline \end{array}$

25. $5 \times 5 = $ _____

Read the problem and follow the directions.

26. Use circles to show what 3×7 means.

27. Look at the groups of stars. Write a multiplication number sentence to represent the groups of stars.

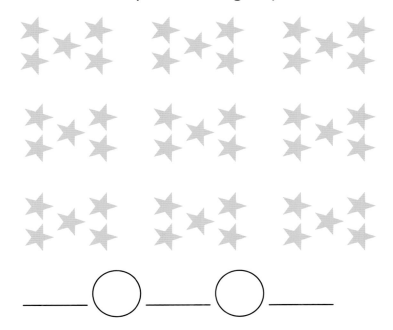

_____ ◯ _____ ◯ _____

28. Write a number sentence for the model.

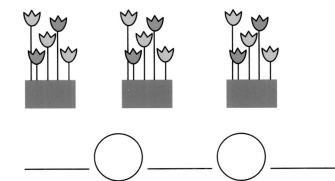

_____ ◯ _____ ◯ _____

29. Use symbols to write a number sentence that means 3 multiplied by 6 equals 18.

_____ ◯ _____ ◯ _____

30. Count by 10s to find the answer to 10×10.

31. Count by 5s to find the answer to 10×5.

32. Sharon does 2 hours of swimming each evening.

Describe the pattern and tell the number of hours of swimming in 7 days.

Rule: times _____							
Number of days	1	2	3	4	5	6	7
Total number of hours swimming	2	4	6	8	10	12	?

Sharon swam for _____ hours after 7 days.

Multiplication Order and Rules

0, 1, and Order

Solve.

1. $7 \times 1 =$ _____

2. $0 \times 9 =$ _____

3. $0 \times 12 =$ _____

4. $50 \times 1 =$ _____

Write the answer. Say your explanation.

5. $6 \times 2 = 12$. What is 2×6? Explain your answer.

$2 \times 6 =$ _____

6. $7 \times 5 = 35$. What is 5×7? Explain your answer.

$5 \times 7 =$ _____

Write the answer.

7. $2 \times 8 = 16$. What is 8×2?

$8 \times 2 =$ _____

8. $3 \times 0 = 0$. What is 0×3?

$0 \times 3 =$ _____

Write the answer. Say your explanation.

9. I am a number. When you show 10 groups of me, the total is 0. What number am I? Explain your answer.

_____

TRY IT

10. I am a number. If you multiply me by 99, the answer is 99. What number am I? Explain your answer.

_____

Multiply the numbers in a different order.
Write the multiplication sentence.

11. $5 \times 4 = 20$

_____ $\times$ _____ $= 20$

12. $7 \times 10 = 70$

_____ $\times$ _____ $= 70$

Circle the expression that has the same answer as the given expression.

13. 5×3

A. 4×3

B. 4×5

C. 5×1

D. 3×5

14. 2×4

A. 1×4

B. 1×2

C. 4×2

D. 4×3

The Commutative Property

Use Properties

Read the problem and follow the directions.

1. Circle the model that has the same sum as 8 + 4.

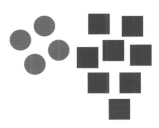  

2. Circle the **two** models that show the same product.

Use the commutative property to solve the problem in your head. Explain how you did it.

3. 39 + 13 + 1 = _____

_____

_____

4. 2 × 7 × 5 = _____

_____

_____

TRY IT

5. Circle the two numbers you would add first to solve this problem in your head. Write why.

$13 + 5 + 2$

_____

_____

6. Find the product in your head. Write how you solved the problem.

$6 \times 0 \times 2 = $ _____

_____

_____

Multiply. Then change the order of the factors to make a new number sentence. Write and solve the new number sentence to check your answer.

7. $5 \times 2 = $ _____

_____

8. $10 \times 5 = $ _____

_____

Write the missing number that makes the number sentence true.

9. $6 + 9 = \boxed{} + 6$

10. $5 \times 7 = 7 \times \boxed{}$

Circle the answer.

11. Erin found the sum of $7 + 6 + 8$. She added $7 + 6$ to get 13 and then added $13 + 8$ to get 21. Which shows a way to check her answer?

   A. $13 + 6 + 8$

   B. $14 + 7 + 6$

   C. $7 + 8 + 6$

   D. $15 + 6 + 8$

12. Peter found the sum of $8 + 6 + 2$. He added $8 + 6$ to get 14 and then added $14 + 2$ to get 16. Which shows a way to check his answer?

   A. $14 + 6 + 2$

   B. $14 + 2 + 6$

   C. $8 + 12 + 2$

   D. $8 + 2 + 6$

TRY IT

The Associative Property

Group Numbers Different Ways

Use squares to show two different ways you could show the grouping of the numbers to find the sum. (Use different colors of squares for each number.) Then write the sum.

1. $9 + 3 + 6 =$ _____

Use squares to show two different ways you could show the grouping of the numbers to find the product. Then write the product.

2. $2 \times 2 \times 4 =$ _____

Write parentheses to show how you would group the numbers to make them easier to add or multiply. Then write the sum or product.

3. $3 + 7 + 7 =$ _____

4. $7 \times 5 \times 2 =$ _____

TRY IT

Say the answer.

5. Use the associative property to solve this problem in your head.
   $4 \times 2 \times 5 = ?$

6. How could knowing the product of $8 \times (4 \times 10)$ help you find the product of $(8 \times 4) \times 10$?

7. Look at this addition problem.

   $(5 + 7) + 1 = 13$

   Would the answer change if you added the 7 and the 1 first and then added the 5? Why or why not?

Read the problem and follow the directions.

8. Solve. Then change the grouping of the numbers to check your work.

   $9 + (4 + 10) = ?$

9. If $3 \times (2 \times 6) = 36$, write the correct product in the box.

   $(3 \times 2) \times 6 = \boxed{}$

10. If $(10 + 2) + 17 = 29$, write the correct sum in the box.

    $10 + (2 + 17) = \boxed{}$

TRY IT

Use Properties

Use Properties to Simplify

Use the commutative property to rewrite each number sentence to make it easier to solve. Then solve the sentence.

1. $29 + 48 + 11 = ?$

Number sentence and work:

_____

$29 + 48 + 11 =$ _____

2. $? = 5 \times 7 \times 2$

Number sentence and work:

_____

_____ $= 5 \times 7 \times 2$

3. $? = 9 \times 8 \times 0$

Number sentence and work:

_____

_____ $= 9 \times 8 \times 0$

4. $18 + 29 + 52 = ?$

Number sentence and work:

_____

$18 + 29 + 52 =$ _____

TRY IT

Use the associative property to rewrite each number sentence to make it easier to solve. Then solve the sentence.

5. $2 \times (3 \times 5) = ?$

Number sentence and work:

_____

$2 \times (3 \times 5) = $ _____

6. $84 + (6 + 7) = ?$

Number sentence and work:

_____

$84 + (6 + 7) = $ _____

7. $? = (36 + 21) + 29$

Number sentence and work:

_____

_____ $= (36 + 21) + 29$

8. $? = (6 \times 5) \times 2$

Number sentence and work:

_____

_____ $= (6 \times 5) \times 2$

TRY IT

Read the problem and follow the directions.

9. Rewrite this number sentence using the associative property. Then solve the first step of the new number sentence.

$(76 + 7) + 23 = ?$

New number sentence:

_____

First step of solving:

_____

10. Which expression shows one way to use the commutative property make this problem easier to solve? Circle the answer.

$2 \times 7 \times 5$

A. $2 \times (7 \times 5)$ B. $2 + 7 \times 5$

C. $2 \times 5 \times 7$ D. $7 - 2 \times 5$

TRY IT

Read the problem and say the answer.

11. Natalie solved this problem: $67 + 25 = 92$.

How could Natalie's work and the commutative property help you find the sum of $25 + 67$?

12. Explain how to use the associative property to make this problem easier to solve.

$(38 + 15) + 5$

13. Lori solved this problem: $52 + 11 = 63$.
Tanner wants to solve to find the sum of $11 + 52$.

How could Tanner use Lori's work and the commutative property to help him find the sum?

TRY IT

Unit Review

Checkpoint Practice

Solve.

1. If $9 \times 6 = 54$, what is 6×9? _____

2. $13 \times 1 =$ _____

3. $0 \times 5 =$ _____

Read the problem and follow the direcctions.

4. Circle the **two** numbers you would multiply first to solve this problem. Write why.

   $2 \times 9 \times 5$

   _____

5. Draw lines to match the property with its definition.

Commutative Property of Addition	You can group the addends in any way and the sum will be the same.
Associative Property of Addition	You can add in any order and the sum will be the same.

6. How can knowing that $(4 \times 3) \times 2 = 24$ help you find $4 \times (3 \times 2)$?

_____

7. Place parentheses in the expression to show what you would multiply first to solve this problem in your head. Write why.

$7 \times 5 \times 2$

_____

8. Draw lines to match the property with its definition.

| Commutative Property of Multiplication | You can multiply in any order and the product will be the same. |

| Associative Property of Multiplication | You can group the factors in any way and the product will be the same. |

Use the commutative or associative property to rewrite each number sentence to make it easier to solve. Then solve.

9. $18 + 19 + 2 =$ _____

10. $(27 + 8) + 12 =$ _____

11. $7 \times 5 \times 2 =$ _____

Write the answer.

12. ☐ is a number.
If ☐ × 2 = 8, what does 2 × ☐ equal?

Explain your answer.

_____

_____

13. I am a number. When I am multiplied by 33 the answer is 33.
What number am I?

_____

14. I am a number. When I am multiplied by 99 the answer is 0.
What number am I?

_____

15. What number goes in the box to make this number
sentence true?

10 × 6 = 6 × ☐   _____

16. What **two** numbers would you add together first to make
this problem easier to solve in your head?

17 + 5 + 3 = ☐   _____

17. Katy said that 3 × 5 = 15. What is another way to do this
problem to check the answer?

_____

18. If you know the product of $5 \times (2 \times 6)$, how can that help you find the product of $(5 \times 2) \times 6$?

_____

_____

_____

19. Use the associative property to solve this problem in your head. Write your answer.

$8 \times 2 \times 5 =$ _____

20. Solve. Then change the grouping of the numbers to check your work.

$(8 + 12) + 4 =$ _____

_____

21. Rewrite this equation using the associative property. Then solve the first step of the new equation.

$5 \times (2 \times 10) = ?$

_____

Division as Repeated Subtraction

Practice Repeated Subtraction

Solve by using repeated subtraction. You may use circles and paper plates.

1. 6 divided by 2 is _____

2. 18 divided by 3 is _____

3. 24 divided by 8 is _____

Solve by using repeated subtraction and a number line.

4. 8 divided by 4 is _____

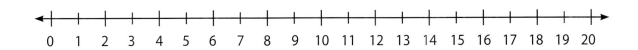

5. 14 divided by 2 is _____

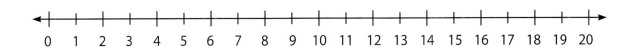

T R Y   I T

6. 12 divided by 4 is _____

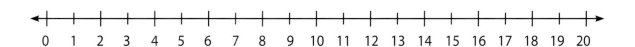

Circle the answer.

7. Stephan solved 15 divided by 3 this way:

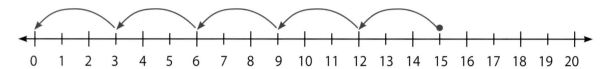

What does 15 divided by 3 equal?

A. 0

B. 3

C. 5

D. 12

Use circles and paper plates to show how to solve the problem.

8. 24 divided by 6 is _____

TRY IT

Division with Repeated Subtraction

Practice Division

Solve with repeated subtraction with a number line.

1. 18 divided by 3 equals _____

2. 15 divided by 5 equals _____

Solve with repeated subtraction. Write the subtraction sentences you use.

3. 10 divided by 5 equals

_____

4. 6 divided by 2 equals

_____

5. 14 divided by 7 equals

_____

6. 12 divided by 3 equals

_____

TRY IT

Read the problem and follow the directions.

7. Jenny has 20 oranges. She wants to give each person 2 oranges.

   Use circles to show how many people will get oranges. Then write the answer. _____ people

8. Cheryl has 15 muffins. She wants to put 3 muffins in each bag.

   How many bags of muffins will she have? Solve with repeated subtraction. Then write the answer. _____ bags

Solve.

9. Jeremy has 12 crackers. He eats 2 crackers each day.

   How many days can Jeremy eat crackers before he eats them all? _____ days

10. Mariah has 24 toys. She can fit 8 toys in 1 basket.

    How many baskets does Mariah need to fit all the toys? _____ baskets

11. Jeff has 16 photos. He puts 4 photos on 1 page of a photo album.

    How many pages does Jeff need for all the pictures? _____ pages

Circle the answer.

12. This is how Carla found 10 divided by 2:
$$10 - 2 = 8$$
$$8 - 2 = 6$$
$$6 - 2 = 4$$
$$4 - 2 = 2$$
$$2 - 2 = 0$$

    What does 10 divided by 2 equal?

    A. 0   B. 2   C. 5   D. 10

TRY IT

Division with Equal Sharing

Practice Equal Shares

Solve. You may use circles and paper plates.

1. There are 6 bananas and 3 friends.
   How many bananas does each friend get?

   6 divided by 3 equals _____

2. There are 16 bananas and 4 friends.
   How many bananas does each friend get?

   16 divided by 4 equals _____

3. There are 9 bananas and 3 friends.
   How many bananas does each friend get?

   _____ bananas

4. There are 12 bananas and 2 friends.
   How many bananas does each friend get?

   _____ bananas

5. 24 divided by 6 equals _____

6. 24 divided by 8 equals _____

TRY IT

7. 24 divided by 12 equals _____

8. 24 divided by 3 equals _____

Read the problem and follow the directions.

9. Show how to divide 20 circles into 5 equal groups.

How many circles are in each group? _____

10. Use circles to divide. Then complete the number sentence.

10 divided by 2 equals _____

11. Maria wants to know the answer to 24 divided by 4. Use circles to make 4 equal groups.

What is the answer to 24 divided by 4? _____

12. Dario wants to know the answer to 20 divided by 4. Use circles to make 4 equal groups.

What is the answer to 20 divided by 4? _____

Equal Share Division

Draw to Divide

Write a number sentence to match the story problem. Then make a drawing to model and solve the number sentence. You can use sketches of circles for the models in the problems. Write the answer.

1. Alexander wants to plant 18 onions. He has 2 garden plots. He wants to plant the same number of onions in each plot.

   How many onions should Alexander plant in each plot?

   _____ divided by _____ equals _?_

   _____ onions

2. Alexander picked 21 carrots. He's going to make 3 big salads. He wants to put the same number of carrots in each salad.

How many carrots should Alexander put in each salad?

__?__ equals _____ divided by _____

_____ carrots

3. Alexander has 6 flower pots. He wants to plant 24 daisies in the pots. Alexander wants to plant the same number of daisies in each pot.

How many daisies should he plant in each pot?

_____ divided by _____ equals __?__

_____ daisies

4. Alexander picked 18 ripe peppers. He wants to give the peppers to his 9 friends. Alexander wants to give the same number of peppers to each friend.

How many peppers should Alexander give to each friend?

_____ divided by _____ equals _?_

[ ]

_____ peppers

---

5. Alexander has 20 tomato plants that he wants to plant in 5 rows. Each row will have the same number of plants.

How many plants will be in each row?

_?_ equals _____ divided by _____

[ ]

_____ tomato plants

6. After a long day on the farm, Alexander decided to put his 24 baseball cards into an album. Each page holds 4 cards.

How many pages will Alexander need?

_?_ equals _____ divided by _____

_____ pages

---

7. Alexander and his grandparents decide to play a card game after dinner. The whole deck of 30 cards is dealt to the 3 players.

How many cards will each player get?

_____ divided by _____ equals _?_

_____ cards

Equal Share Division

Practice Story Problems

Write a number sentence to match the story problem.
Then circle equal groups in the picture and solve the
number sentence. Write the answer.

1. If 6 boys shared these marbles equally, how many
   would each boy get?

   _?_ equals _____ divided by _____

   _____ marbles

2. If 2 girls shared these stickers equally, how many
   would each girl get?

   _____ divided by _____ equals _?_

   _____ stickers

TRY IT

Write a number sentence to match the story problem.
Then use circles to model and solve the number
sentence. Write the answer.

3. Sam has 20 books. He wants to put the same
   number of books on each of the 4 shelves. How
   many books should be on each shelf?

   _?_ equals _____ divided by _____

   _____ books

4. A piñata has 25 pieces of candy in it. 5 children
   equally share the candy. How many pieces will
   each child get?

   _____ divided by _____ equals _?_

   _____ pieces of candy

5. Linda has 15 crayons. She wants to put them into
   3 boxes, with each box having the same number
   of crayons. How many crayons should she put in
   each box?

   _?_ equals _____ divided by _____

   _____ crayons

TRY IT

Write the answer.

6. Tom solved 12 divided by 3 this way:

What is the answer to 12 divided by 3?

12 divided by 3 equals _____

Circle the answer. You may use circles or drawings.

7. 5 children want to share these grapes equally.
How many grapes will each child get?

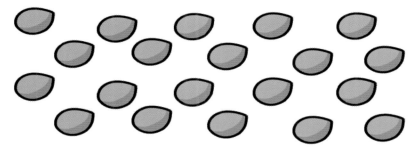

A. 4	B. 5
C. 6	D. 20

---

8. 8 children want to share 24 oranges equally.
How many oranges will each child get?

A. 2	B. 3
C. 8	D. 16

T R Y I T

9. Which picture shows how 8 children could share
16 toy cars equally?

A.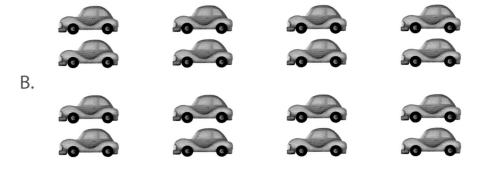

B.

C.

D.

Represent Division

Division Sentences

Draw a picture or number line sketch for the division sentence.

1. $12 \div 6 = 2$

2. $10 \div 5 = 2$

3. $30 \div 5 = 6$

4. $14 \div 2 = 7$

TRY IT

Write a division sentence to match the picture.

5.

_____

6.

_____

Write a division sentence to match the story problem and include the answer in your division sentence.

7. 16 crayons are divided equally in 4 boxes.

   _____

8. 24 children get into 3 equal groups.

   _____

9. 6 strawberries are shared equally among 3 friends.

   _____

10. 40 books are placed equally among 5 shelves.

   _____

TRY IT

Circle the answer.

11. Eddy wrote the problem 12 ÷ 4. What operation should he use to solve the problem?

   A. division

   B. multiplication

   C. addition

   D. subtraction

---

12. Which symbol should be placed in the circle to show 6 divided by 2?

   6 2

   A. +

   B. ×

   C. ÷

   D. −

TRY IT

Remainders in Division

Remainders in Story Problems

Complete the number sentence to match the story problem.
Then use circles and paper plates to model and solve the number
sentence. Write the answer.

1. There are 18 bones and 4 dogs.
   Each dog will get the same number of bones.

   How many bones will each dog get?

   _____ ÷ _____ = $\underline{?}$

   _____ bones

Complete the number sentence to match the story
problem. Then make a sketch to solve the number sentence.
Write the answer.

2. Lilly's dog has 11 tennis balls.
   A container can hold 3 tennis balls.
   Lilly fills as many containers as she can.

   How many tennis balls are left over?

   _____ ÷ _____ = $\underline{?}$

   _____ tennis balls

3. Avery baked 11 dog treats.
He will share the treats equally among 5 dogs.
He will save the leftover treats.

How many dog treats will Avery save?

_____ ÷ _____ = $\frac{?}{}$

_____ of the treats

Complete the number sentence to match the story problem.
Then use the number line and repeated subtraction to model
and solve the number sentence. Write the answer.

4. Colin's family is giving 15 bowls to a dog shelter.
Each dog at the shelter needs 2 bowls.

How many dogs can receive 2 bowls from Colin's family?

_____ ÷ _____ = $\frac{?}{}$

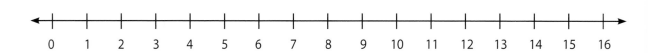

_____ dogs

Remainders in Division

Practice with Remainders

Use circles and paper plates to model and solve the number sentence. Write the answer.

1. $9 \div 2 =$ _____ r _____

2. $16 \div 9 =$ _____ r _____

Use the number line and repeated subtraction to model and solve the number sentence. Write the answer.

3. $17 \div 3 =$ _____ r _____

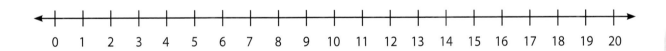

4. $20 \div 8 =$ _____ r _____

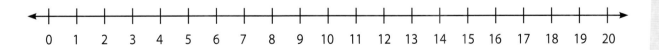

TRY IT

Use circles to model and solve the story problem. Say your answer.

5. There are 13 blankets.
   If 3 people will share the blankets equally, how many blankets will each person get?

   How many blankets will be left over?

6. Hannah's family has a box of 23 oranges.
   The family eats 4 oranges every day.

   How many oranges will be left in the box on the last day?

Circle the answer.

7. Which picture shows how 3 people could share 16 stickers equally and how many stickers will be left over?

A.

B.

C.

Unit Review

Checkpoint Practice

Solve with repeated subtraction and a number line.

1. $14 \div$ by $2 =$ _____

2. $12 \div 3 =$ _____

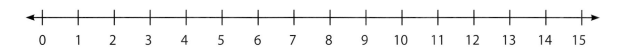

Solve with repeated subtraction. You may use circles.
Record your subtraction.

3. $8 \div 2 =$ _____

4. $24 \div 3 =$ _____

UNIT REVIEW

Solve with equal sharing. You may use circles.

5. $18 \div 6 =$ _____

6. $12 \div 2 =$ _____

7. There are 20 books and 5 children.
   How many books does each child get?

   $20 \div 5 =$ _____

8. If 4 girls share 24 stickers equally,
   how many would each girl get?

   $24 \div 4 =$ _____

9. Draw a picture for this division sentence.
   $15 \div 5 = 3$

10. Write a division sentence for this model.

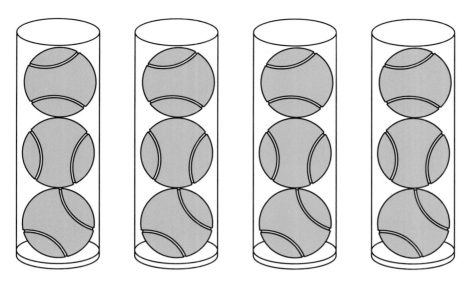

_____

Solve.

11. 5 girls want to share 13 dolls equally.

How many dolls will each girl get? _____

How many dolls will be left over? _____

12. Terrance has 20 crayons.
He puts an equal number in each of 3 boxes
How many crayons are left over?

_____ crayons

Read the problem and follow the directions.

13. Use repeated subtraction to solve.

Felipe has a box of 24 crayons and wants to give 2 crayons to each person.

How many people will get crayons?

_____ people

14. Use the number line to solve.

Maribel wants to buy 18 juice boxes. The juice boxes are sold with 6 boxes in each package.

How many packages of juice boxes does Maribel need to buy?

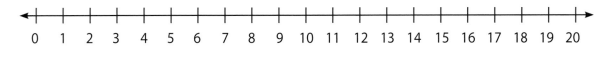

0 1 2 3 4 5 6 7 8 9 10 11 12 13 14 15 16 17 18 19 20

_____ packages

15. 5 children want to share 20 pennies equally.

How many pennies will each child get? Circle the answer.

A. 4

B. 5

C. 10

D. 20

16. Barbie wants to divide 15 cherries into 5 equal groups. Draw a sketch to show how many cherries will be in each group.

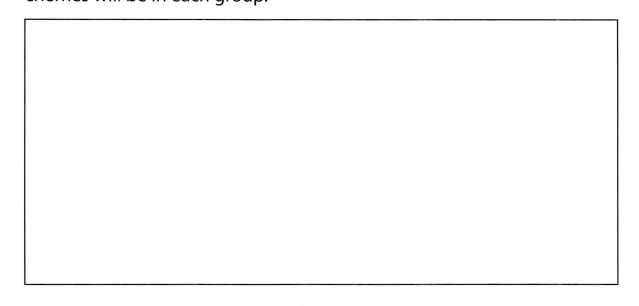

17. Write a division sentence for the model.

_____

18. Look at the symbol where the arrow is pointing.

What does this symbol mean? Say the answer.

$$12 \div 4 = 3$$

19. Which symbol goes in the circle to make the number sentence true? Circle the answer.

12  6 = 2

A. +

B. −

C. ×

D. ÷

20. 6 children are playing tennis.
There are 22 tennis balls.

If the children share the tennis balls equally, how many will each child get and how many will be left over?

_____ tennis balls each

_____ tennis balls left over

Display Data

Same Data, Different Displays

Read the problem and follow the directions.

1. The tally chart shows 18 students' favorite art supplies.

   The picture graph shows the same data as the tally chart.

   Explain how you know the two graphs show the same data.

Favorite Art Supply	
Types of Supplies	**Tally**
Chalk	||
Crayons	||||
Paintbrush	|||||||
Markers	||||

_____

_____

_____

_____

_____

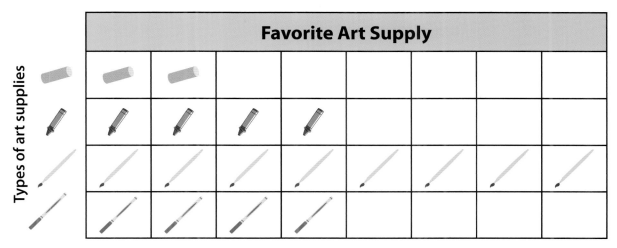

Favorite Art Supply

Types of art supplies

Number of votes for art supplies
Each picture in the boxes equals 1.

L E A R N

2. The picture graph and the tally chart in Problem 1 show the same data.

Circle the answer that also shows these same data.

A.

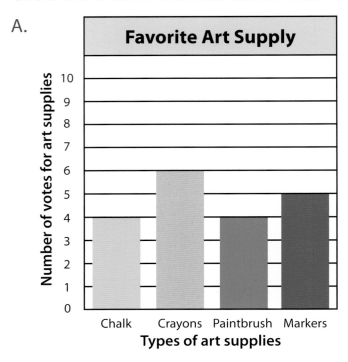

B.

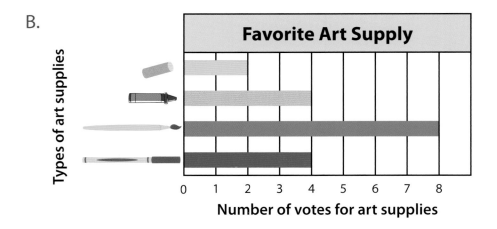

3. The picture graph shows 20 students' favorite toys with wheels. Circle the bar graph that shows the same data set as the picture graph.

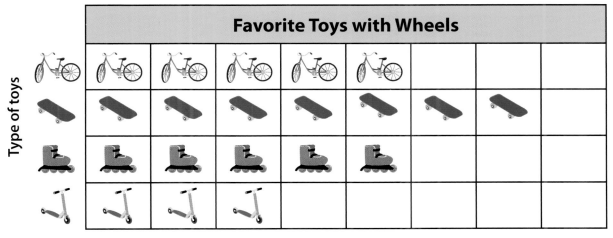

Number of toys

Each picture in the boxes equals 1.

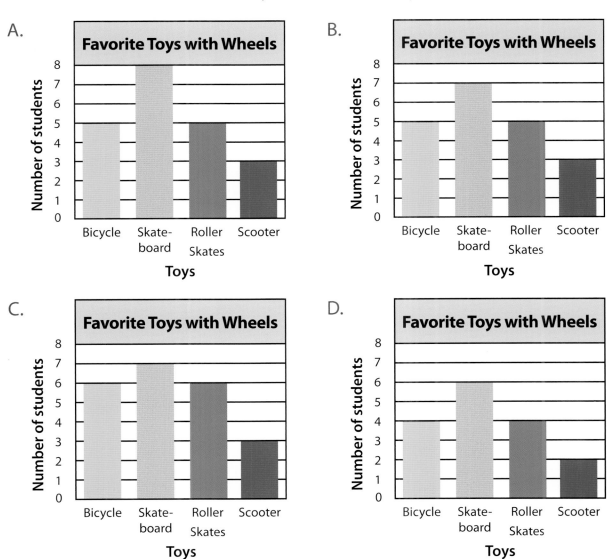

A.

Favorite Toys with Wheels

B.

Favorite Toys with Wheels

C.

Favorite Toys with Wheels

D.

Favorite Toys with Wheels

4. The tally chart shows 13 students' favorite fruit. Create your own vertical bar graph that shows the same data.

Favorite Fruit	
Favorite Fruit	**Tally**
Banana	|||
Orange	||||
Apple	~~||||~~ |

LEARN

Display Data

Make Graphs and Charts

Read the problem and follow the directions.

1. Make a tally chart to show the data set. Remember to label all parts of your chart.

_____	Tally

2. Missy has 4 stickers with hearts, 7 stickers with stars, and 6 stickers with smiling faces. Make a picture graph to show Missy's stickers.

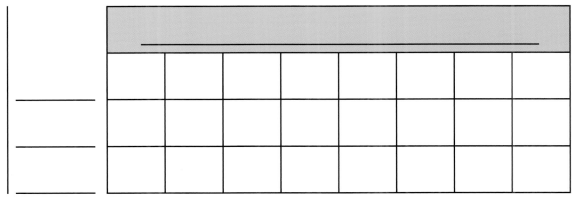

Number of stickers
Each picture in the boxes equals 1.

TRY IT

3. Make a bar graph to show the same data as in the tally chart.

Favorite Berries	
Strawberries 🍓	||||
Raspberries 🫐	||||
Blueberries ⬤	|||| |

4. Draw a picture graph to show the data in this tally chart.

Favorite Fruit	
Fruit	**Number**
Oranges	||||
Apples	|||
Pears	|||| |

Number of votes for fruit
Each picture in the boxes equals 1.

TRY IT

Circle the answer.

5. Which tally chart shows the correct number of toys shown here?

A.

Tom's Toy Shop	
Toy	Tally
🪀	IIII
🧸	III
🧍	⊬II

B.

Tom's Toy Shop	
Toy	Tally
🪀	III
🧸	⊬
🧍	IIII

C.

Tom's Toy Shop	
Toy	Tally
🪀	⊬
🧸	IIII
🧍	III

D.

Tom's Toy Shop	
Toy	Tally
🪀	IIII
🧸	⊬
🧍	III

6. This bar graph shows how many books were sold each day at a bookstore. Which picture graph shows the same data as the bar graph?

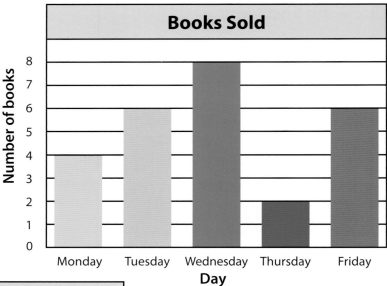

A.

Books Sold	
Day	**Number of Books**
Monday	📖 📖 📖 📖 📖 📖
Tuesday	📖 📖 📖 📖
Wednesday	📖 📖 📖 📖 📖 📖 📖 📖
Thursday	📖 📖 📖 📖
Friday	📖 📖

B.

Books Sold	
Day	**Number of Books**
Monday	📖 📖 📖 📖
Tuesday	📖 📖 📖 📖 📖 📖 📖
Wednesday	📖 📖
Thursday	📖 📖 📖 📖 📖 📖
Friday	📖 📖 📖 📖 📖 📖 📖

C.

Books Sold	
Day	**Number of Books**
Monday	📖 📖 📖 📖
Tuesday	📖 📖 📖 📖 📖 📖
Wednesday	📖 📖 📖 📖 📖 📖 📖 📖
Thursday	📖 📖
Friday	📖 📖 📖 📖 📖 📖

TRY IT

Data Questions

Chart and Graph Questions

Use the picture graph for Problems 1–3. The picture graph shows students' responses when they were asked to name their favorite flower.

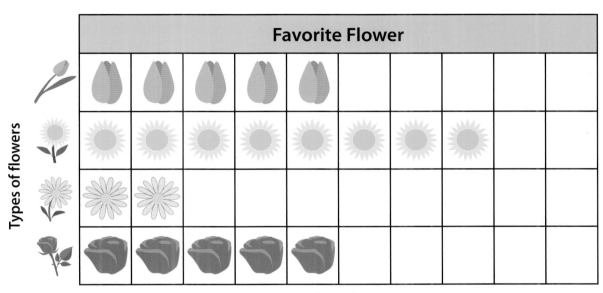

Favorite Flower

Types of flowers

Number of votes

Each picture in the boxes equals 1.

1. How many students like sunflowers the most?

_____

2. Circle the flower that got the fewest votes.

3. Write a different question about the Favorite Flower graph.

_____

_____

_____

TRY IT

Use the bar graph for Problems 4–6. The graph shows students' responses when they were asked what kind of pet they have.

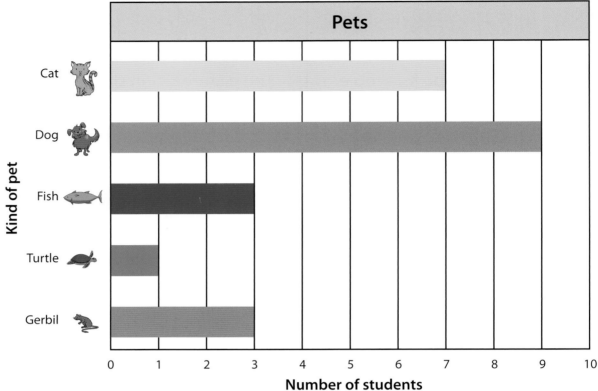

4. How many students have cats?

_____

5. How many more students have dogs than gerbils?

_____

6. Write a different question about the Pets graph and answer it.

_____

_____

_____

_____

_____

Read the problem and follow the directions.

Lemonade Sold	
Day	**Tally**
Monday	|||
Tuesday	|||||	
Wednesday	||||| ||

7. Write a question that could be answered with information from the graph and then answer it.

_____

_____

_____

_____

8. Look at the graph. Write a question that could be answered with information from the graph.

_____

_____

_____

_____

_____

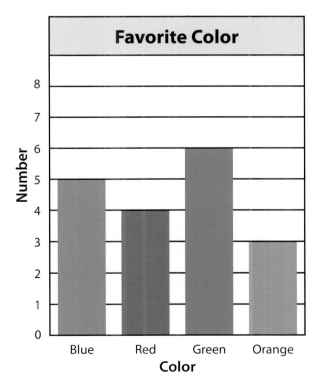

T R Y   I T

9. Look at the tally chart. Write a question that could be answered with information from the tally chart and then answer it.

Favorite Muffin	
Muffin	**Tally**
Strawberry	卌 ||
Blueberry	卌
Lemon	卌 卌	
Orange	卌 |||

_____

_____

_____

_____

TRY IT

Use Data to Solve Problems

Problems About Data

Use the graph or chart to write and solve a number sentence for the problem. Then write the answer.

1.

Bags of Popcorn Sold	
Size of Bag	Number of Bags
Small	卌 |||
Medium	|||
Large	卌

How many small and medium bags of popcorn were sold in all?

Number sentence: _____

Answer: _____ small and medium bags

How many fewer medium bags than large bags of popcorn were sold?

Number sentence: _____

Answer: _____ fewer medium bags

2.

Animals										
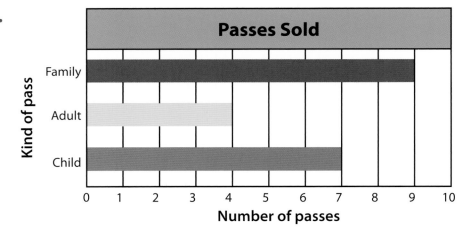										

Types of animals

Number of animals

Each picture in the boxes equals 1.

How many more giraffes than lions are there?

Number sentence: _____

Answer: _____ more giraffes

How many lions and zebras are there altogether?

Number sentence: _____

Answer: _____ lions and zebras

3.

Passes Sold

Kind of pass

Family

Adult

Child

0   1   2   3   4   5   6   7   8   9   10

Number of passes

How many fewer adult passes than child passes were sold?

Number sentence: _____

Answer: _____ fewer adult passes

TRY IT

How many passes of all kinds were sold?

Number sentence: _____

Answer: _____ passes of all kinds

4.

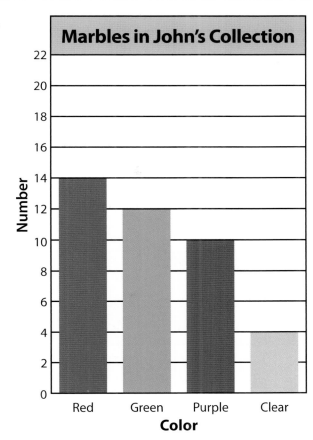

How many red and purple marbles are in John's collection?

Number sentence: _____

Answer: _____ red and purple marbles

Circle the answer.

5.

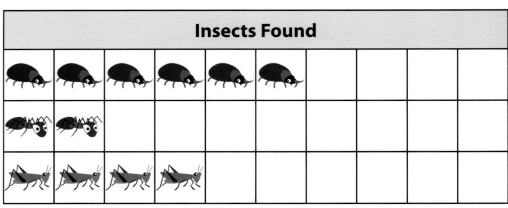

Insects Found									

Types of insects

Beetles 🪲🪲🪲🪲🪲🪲

Ants 🐜🐜

Crickets 🦗🦗🦗🦗

Number of insects

Each picture in the boxes equals 1.

Which number sentence could be used to figure out how many more beetles than crickets were found?

A. $6 + 4 = ?$ B. $6 - 4 = ?$

C. $6 \times 2 = ?$ D. $6 - 2 = ?$

6.

Number of Animals in the Zoo										

Types of animals

Zebra 🦓🦓🦓

Elephant 🐘

Alligator 🐊🐊🐊

Monkey 🐵🐵🐵🐵🐵

Number of animals

Each picture in the boxes equals 1.

Which number sentence could be used to figure out how many animals are in the zoo?

A. $5 \times 3 = ?$ B. $5 + 3 = ?$

C. $3 + 3 + 5 = ?$ D. $3 + 1 + 3 + 5 = ?$

TRY IT

Range and Mode of Data Sets

Range and Mode

Use the table for Problems 1 and 2.

Softball Team Roster	
Name	**Age**
Vicky	11
Becky	9
Molly	10
Hannah	9
Tori	8
Emma	7
Lauren	7
Kayla	8
Teresa	8

1. Circle the youngest age and the oldest age in the table.

   What is the range of the ages on the softball team?

   _____ years

2. Write the numbers in the table in order from least to greatest.

   _____

   What is the mode of the ages?

   _____ years

T R Y   I T

Use the table for Problems 3 and 4.

Bowling Scores									
85	90	100	85	65	70	85	60	85	95

3. What is the range of the data?

_____

4. What is the mode of the data?

_____

Write the answer.

5. Here are the ages in years of the members of the Fields family:

   50, 10, 6, 12, 42

   What is the range of the ages of the family members?

   _____ years

6. What is the range of this set of numbers?

   99, 65, 78, 71, 91, 100

   _____

Circle the answer.

7. Dora asked her friends how many dolls they have. Here are the numbers of dolls that 10 of Dora's friends have:

   4, 6, 6, 5, 8, 5, 7, 7, 5, 5

   What is the mode of the number of dolls Dora's friends have?

   A. 4   B. 5   C. 6   D. 7

8. What is the mode of the following data set?

   10, 12, 11, 11, 8, 12, 12, 8, 10, 12, 12, 11, 8

   A. 12   B. 8   C. 10   D. 11

Unit Review

Checkpoint Practice

Make a bar graph to show the same data as those in the tally chart. Be sure to put the title and all labels on your graph.

1.

Favorite Sport	
Type of Sport	**Number of Votes**
Soccer	~~HHH~~ |||
Basketball	||||
Baseball	~~HHH~~	

Use the bar graph for Problems 2–5.

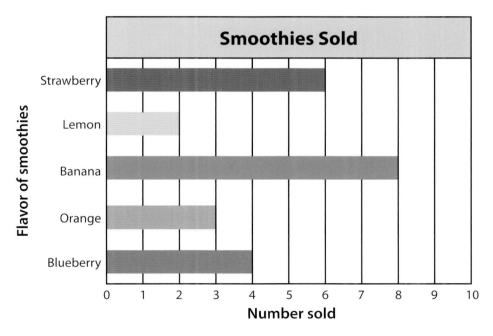

2. How many banana smoothies were sold?

_____

3. How many more strawberry smoothies than blueberry smoothies were sold?

_____

UNIT REVIEW

4. Write and solve a number sentence that shows how many fewer orange smoothies than banana smoothies were sold.

_____

5. Write a different question about the Smoothies Sold bar graph and answer it.

_____

_____

_____

_____

Use the data for Problems 6 and 7. The data set shows high scorers on a computer game.

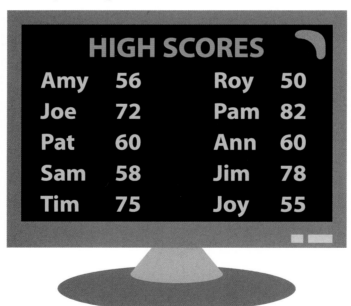

HIGH SCORES

Amy	56	Roy	50
Joe	72	Pam	82
Pat	60	Ann	60
Sam	58	Jim	78
Tim	75	Joy	55

6. What is the range for this data set?

_____

7. What is the mode of the scores?

_____

Read the problem and follow the directions.

8. Create a tally chart to record the number of each type of ball shown here.

_____	_____
_____	_____

9. The bar graph records the number of turtles Raymond saw at the zoo.

Draw a picture graph to record the same data.

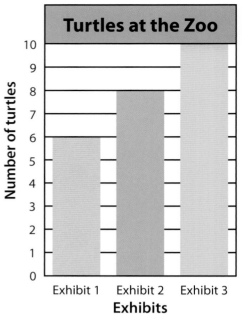

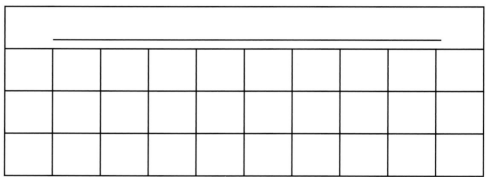

10. Write a question that could be answered with information from the graph and then answer it.

_____

_____

_____

_____

_____

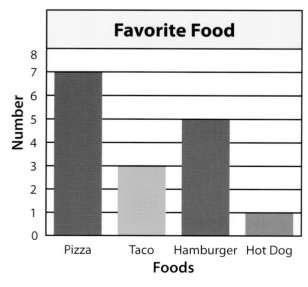

11. Look at the graph. Write a question that could be answered with information from the graph.

Plums Eaten	
Sheri	🫐 🫐 🫐 🫐 🫐 🫐
Cole	🫐 🫐 🫐 🫐 🫐
Isabel	🫐 🫐 🫐 🫐 🫐 🫐 🫐

Number of plums

🫐 equals 1 plum.

_____

_____

_____

Circle the answer.

12. Use the graph to answer the question. Which number sentence could be used to figure out how many animals are in the zoo?

Number of Animals in the Zoo									
Zebra	🦓	🦓	🦓	🦓	🦓				
Elephant	🐘	🐘	🐘	🐘					
Alligator	🐊	🐊							
Monkey	🐒	🐒	🐒						

Number of animals

Each picture in the boxes equals 1.

A. $5 - 2 = ?$

B. $5 + 4 + 2 + 3 = ?$

C. $5 - 3 = ?$

D. $3 + 4 + 5 = ?$

13. Use the graph to answer the question.
Which number sentence could be used to figure out how many more zebras than elephants are in the zoo?

Number of Animals in the Zoo			
Zebra			
Zebra	Alligator		
Zebra	Alligator		Monkey
Zebra	Alligator	Elephant	Monkey
Zebras	Alligators	Elephants	Monkeys

Number of animals

Types of animals
Each picture in the boxes equals 1.

A. $4 + 1 = ?$

B. $4 - 1 = ?$

C. $4 - 3 = ?$

D. $4 + 3 = ?$

---

14. What is the range of these data?

15, 21, 65, 13, 12, 55

A. 12

B. 53

C. 65

D. 77

---

15. What is the mode of the following data set?

4, 4, 2, 2, 4, 3, 3

A. 2

B. 3

C. 4

D. 7

Fractional Parts of a Whole

Parts of a Whole

Circle the picture that matches the description.

1. 5 of 8 parts shaded

   A.   B.   C.

2. 1 whole shaded

   A.   B.   C.

3. $\frac{4}{6}$ shaded

   A.   B.   C.

Circle the fraction that names the shaded part of the shape.

4.

   A. $\frac{2}{4}$

   B. $\frac{1}{4}$

   C. $\frac{1}{3}$

5.

   A. $\frac{2}{3}$

   B. $\frac{2}{1}$

   C. $\frac{3}{3}$

TRY IT

6.

    A. $\frac{1}{3}$

    B. $\frac{1}{2}$

    C. $\frac{3}{3}$

7.

    A. $\frac{2}{3}$

    B. $\frac{2}{5}$

    C. $\frac{2}{4}$

Circle the answer.

8. What fraction of this shape is shaded?

    A. $\frac{1}{8}$ B. $\frac{8}{1}$ C. $\frac{1}{7}$ D. $\frac{7}{1}$

9. Which shows $\frac{3}{4}$ shaded?

    A.   B. 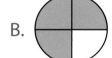   C.

10. Which fraction is equal to 1 whole?

    A. $\frac{1}{3}$ B. $\frac{2}{3}$ C. $\frac{2}{8}$ D. $\frac{4}{4}$

Say the answer.

11. What fraction of this rectangle is shaded? Explain your answer.

12. What is another way of saying $\frac{2}{2}$? Explain your answer.

TRY IT

Fractional Parts and 1 Whole

Parts and Wholes

Read the problem and follow the directions.

1. Color the flowers that show a fraction that equals 1 whole.

2. Color the parts of the number line to equal 1 whole.

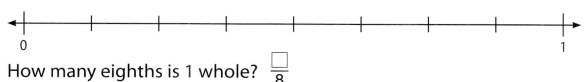

How many eighths is 1 whole? $\dfrac{\square}{8}$

Circle the answer.

3. Which fraction is equal to 1 whole?

A. $\dfrac{5}{5}$

B. $\dfrac{2}{8}$

C. $\dfrac{1}{8}$

D. $\dfrac{2}{7}$

TRY IT

4. Each circle is divided into equal parts. Which circle shows 1 whole shaded?

A.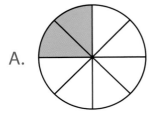

B.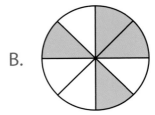

C.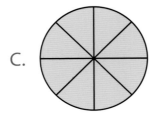

D.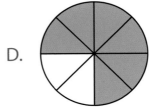

Say the answer.

5. Jake cut his toast into 4 equal pieces. If he eats all 4 pieces, how much of the toast will Jake have eaten? Explain your answer.

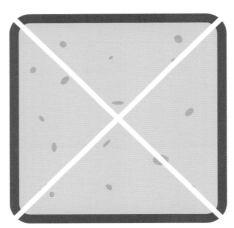

6. What is another way of saying $\frac{7}{7}$? Explain your answer.

TRY IT

Fractions and Whole Numbers

Plot Fractions

Label each tick mark on the number line with the correct fraction.

1.

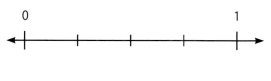

_____ _____ _____ _____ _____

2.

_____ _____ _____ _____ _____ _____ _____

3.

_____ _____ _____ _____ _____ _____ _____

4.

_____ _____ _____ _____ _____

5.

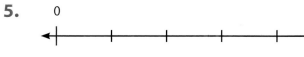

_____ _____ _____ _____ _____ _____ _____ _____ _____ _____ _____

Plot the shaded fraction on the number line and write the fraction underneath.

6.

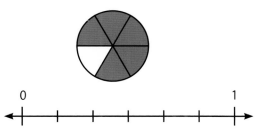

7.

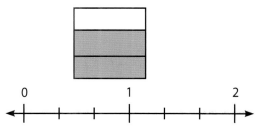

T R Y   I T

Draw an arrow that points to where the fraction is located on the number line.

8. $\frac{3}{4}$

9. $\frac{1}{5}$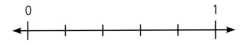

10. $\frac{3}{8}$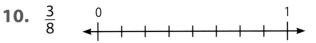

Circle the answer.

11. Which number line shows an arrow pointing to $\frac{3}{2}$?

A.

B.

C.

12. Which number line shows an arrow pointing to $\frac{6}{4}$?

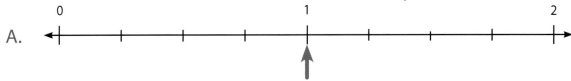

A.

B.

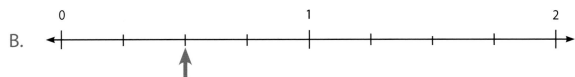

C.

Model and Compare Fractions

Fraction Practice

Shade parts of the shape to model the fraction.

1. $\frac{6}{10}$

2. $\frac{7}{8}$

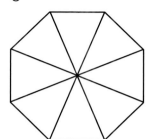

Shade objects in the set to model the fraction.

3. $\frac{11}{12}$

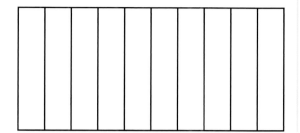

4. $\frac{2}{9}$

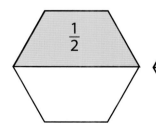

Plot a point on the number line to show where the fraction is located.

5. $\frac{3}{6}$

0   1

6. $1\frac{2}{3}$

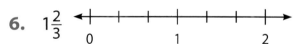

0   1   2

Circle the greater fraction.

7.

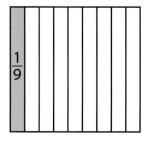

$\frac{1}{9}$ $\frac{1}{5}$

8.

$\frac{1}{2}$ $\frac{1}{6}$

TRY IT

Circle the lesser fraction.

9.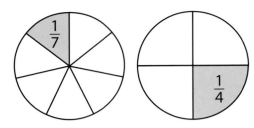

10.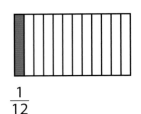

$\frac{1}{12}$ $\frac{1}{8}$

Compare the fractions. Write > or < in the box.

11. $\frac{1}{10}$ ☐ $\frac{1}{4}$

12. $\frac{1}{6}$ ☐ $\frac{1}{11}$

13. $\frac{1}{6}$ ☐ $\frac{1}{5}$

14. $\frac{1}{12}$ ☐ $\frac{1}{10}$

Circle the answer.

15. Which fraction is the greatest?

   A. $\frac{1}{4}$ B. $\frac{1}{3}$ C. $\frac{1}{9}$ D. $\frac{1}{7}$

16. Jack made 4 pizzas. Each pizza is exactly the same size. He cut each pizza into a different number of pieces.

Jack's mom said he could have 1 piece of pizza. He wants to take the largest piece. From which pizza would Jack get the largest piece?

A.

B.

C.

D.

Equivalent Fractions

Practice Equivalent Fractions

Use blocks to model the given fraction. Then use the blocks to model an equivalent fraction with the given denominator. The yellow hexagon is 1 whole for Problems 1–4. Write the numerator of the equivalent fraction.

1. $1 = \dfrac{\boxed{}}{6}$

2. $\dfrac{1}{3} = \dfrac{\boxed{}}{6}$

3. $\dfrac{3}{6} = \dfrac{\boxed{}}{2}$

4. $\dfrac{4}{6} = \dfrac{\boxed{}}{3}$

Shade the shape to show a fraction that is equivalent to the given fraction.

5.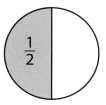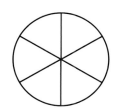

6.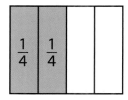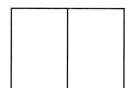

7.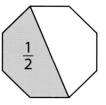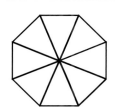

8.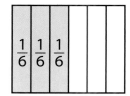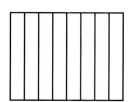

TRY IT

Write a fraction on the bottom number line that is equivalent to the fraction on the top number line.

9. $\dfrac{1}{3} = \dfrac{\boxed{}}{\boxed{}}$

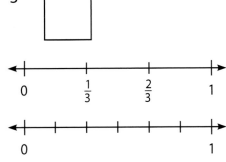

10. $1\dfrac{1}{2} = \boxed{}\ \dfrac{\boxed{}}{\boxed{}}$

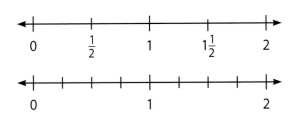

Write a fraction that is equivalent to the given fraction.

11. $\dfrac{5}{10} = $ _____

12. $\dfrac{4}{8} = $ _____

13. $\dfrac{2}{4} = $ _____

Circle the answer.

14. Which fraction is equivalent to $\dfrac{1}{2}$?

   A. $\dfrac{3}{4}$ B. $\dfrac{3}{8}$

   C. $\dfrac{1}{3}$ D. $\dfrac{4}{8}$

15. Which fraction is equivalent to $\dfrac{3}{6}$?

   A. $\dfrac{2}{4}$ B. $\dfrac{4}{9}$

   C. $\dfrac{3}{8}$ D. $\dfrac{8}{4}$

16. Which rectangle shows the same amount shaded as the one below?

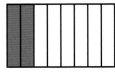

  A. 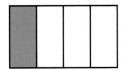   B.    C.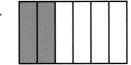

TRY IT

Unit Review

Checkpoint Practice

Write the fraction that names the shaded part of the shape or set.

1. _____

2. _____

3. _____

4. _____

5. _____

6. _____

7. _____

Plot the shaded fraction on the number line and write the fraction underneath.

8.

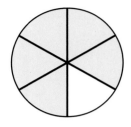

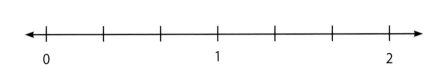

9.

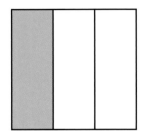

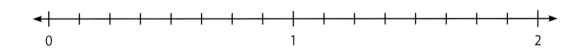

Plot the fraction or whole number on the number line.

10. $\frac{1}{8}$

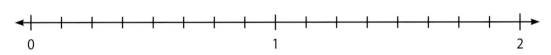

11. 2

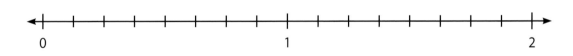

12. $1\frac{3}{8}$

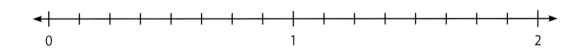

13. $\frac{1}{2}$

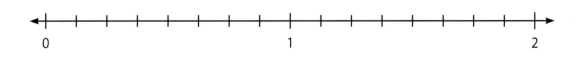

14. $\frac{5}{8}$

Shade part of the shape or objects in the set to model the fraction.

15. $\frac{4}{10}$

16. $\frac{1}{7}$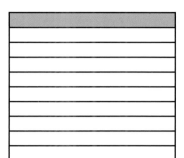

Compare the fractions. Write >, <, or = in the box.

17. $\frac{1}{6}$ ☐ $\frac{1}{10}$

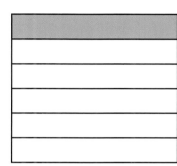

18. $\frac{2}{4}$ ☐ $\frac{4}{8}$

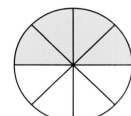

19. $\frac{2}{2}$ ☐ $\frac{6}{6}$

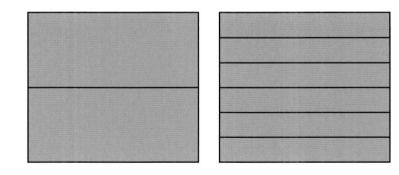

20. $\frac{1}{2}$ ☐ $\frac{1}{4}$

21. $\frac{1}{5}$ ☐ $\frac{1}{3}$

UNIT REVIEW

Use blocks to solve Problems 22 and 23.

22. Cover $\frac{2}{6}$ of the hexagon.

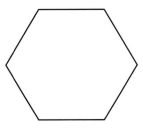

23. Model $\frac{3}{6}$. Then use the blocks to model an equivalent fraction with the denominator 2. Write the numerator of the equivalent fraction.

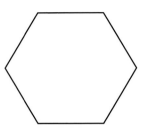

$\frac{3}{6} = \dfrac{\boxed{}}{2}$

Write the answer.

24. Write the fraction one-sixth.

_____

25. Which fraction is greater, $\frac{1}{5}$ or $\frac{1}{2}$?

_____

26. Which fraction is greater, $\frac{1}{10}$ or $\frac{1}{6}$?

_____

Say the name of the fraction.

27. $\frac{1}{8}$

28. $\frac{1}{3}$

29. $\frac{1}{5}$

UNIT REVIEW

Semester Review

Checkpoint Practice

Use circle blocks to model the problem. Write the answer.

1. 6 children are playing tennis.
    There are 22 tennis balls.

    If the children share the tennis balls
    equally, how many will each child get? _____ balls for each child

    How many will be left over? _____ balls left over

2. 4 children want to share 24 balloons equally.
    How many will each child get?

    After modeling the problem,
    show your model on the sketch. _____ balloons for each child

3. $4 \times 10 =$ _____

4. $3 \times 5 =$ _____

Use 1 yellow hexagon and 2 blue rhombuses to make the model. Write the answer.

5. Put the blue rhombuses on top of the yellow hexagon.

What fraction of the yellow shape is covered by the blue shapes? _____

Put the blocks in a row in front of you.
Use the blocks to answer the problem.

6. Circle the solid figures that have triangular faces.

Say the answer.

7. What is another way of saying $\frac{5}{5}$? Explain your answer.

8. Diane knows the sum of $31 + 22$.

How can she use that information to find the sum of $22 + 31$?

9. Solve the problem. Explain why you added or why you subtracted.

The jewelry store sold 304 bracelets in one month. The following month it sold 536 bracelets.

How many bracelets did it sell in two months?

10. How are all these shapes different?

Write the answer.

11. What fraction of the set is made up of shaded stars? _____

12. Use repeated subtraction to solve the problem.

Seth has 15 blocks. He makes towers with 3 blocks each. How many towers does Seth make?

Repeated subtraction sentences:

_____

_____

_____

_____

_____ _____ towers

13. Write the missing number to make the number sentence true.

$4 + 5 = $ _____ $+ 4$

14. Write a multiplication sentence for the model.

_____

15. Write a number sentence that could be used to solve this problem.

A pet store has 273 fish in one large tank and 96 fish in another tank. How many fish are there in the two tanks?

_____

16. Order the numbers from least to greatest using the symbol $<$.

509, 611, 602, 755

_____

17. Write three different numbers that are less than 1,000. Each number should have a 4 in the hundreds place and a 7 in the ones place.

_____   _____   _____

18. Write the number 622 in expanded form.

_____

19. Show an array for the multiplication problem 5×2.

Draw an arrow that points to where the fraction is located on the number line.

20. $\frac{4}{7}$

Plot a point to show the fraction or whole number on the number line.

21. $\frac{3}{5}$

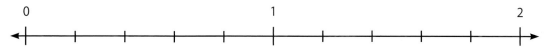

22. $1\frac{2}{5}$

Circle the answer.

23. Which fraction represents one-sixth?

    A. $\frac{1}{6}$ B. $\frac{1}{2}$ C. $\frac{1}{7}$ D. $\frac{1}{12}$

24. What fraction of this set is circled?

    A. $\frac{1}{4}$ B. $\frac{1}{3}$ C. $\frac{4}{1}$ D. $\frac{1}{5}$

25. How many pictures did Camille and Patrick paint altogether?

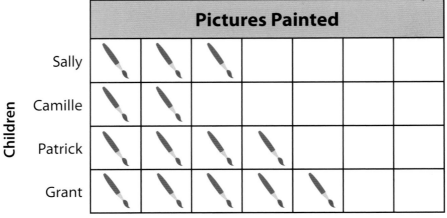

Key: Each picture in the boxes = 1.

A. 2   B. 4   C. 6   D. 9

26. Jaime flew a total of 834 miles on two flights. The first flight was 166 miles. How long was the second flight?

A. 1,000   B. 768   C. 732   D. 668

27. Subtract.

501
− 211

A. 290   B. 712   C. 310   D. 299

28. Add.

405
+ 327

A. 732   B. 727   C. 722   D. 712

29. Which shape has 3 sides?

A.   B.   C.   D.

10-Section Spinner

Position the tip of a pencil or pen inside a paper clip on the center of the spinner and use your finger to spin the paper clip.

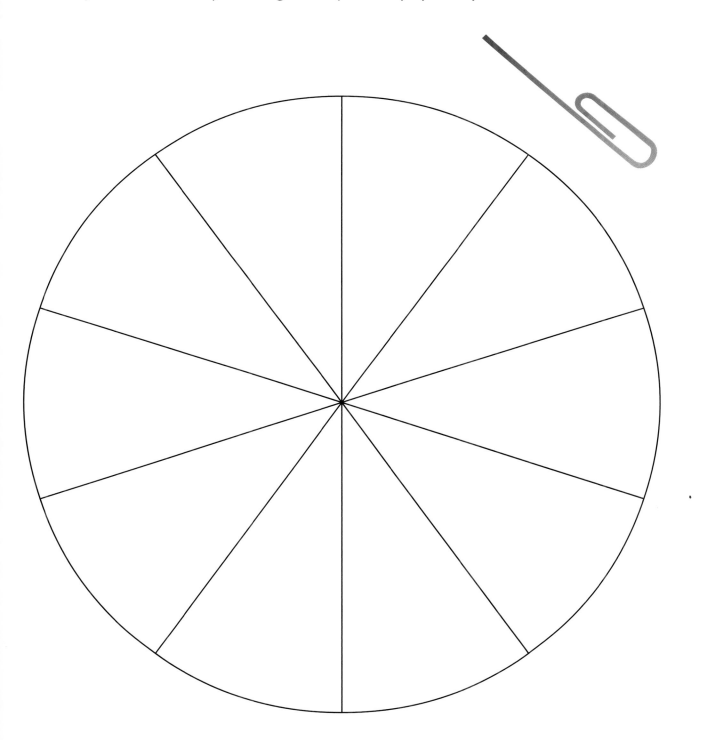

Fact Family Triangles

Use the blank fact family triangles to write fact families.
Cut out each triangle and put the black dot at the top.

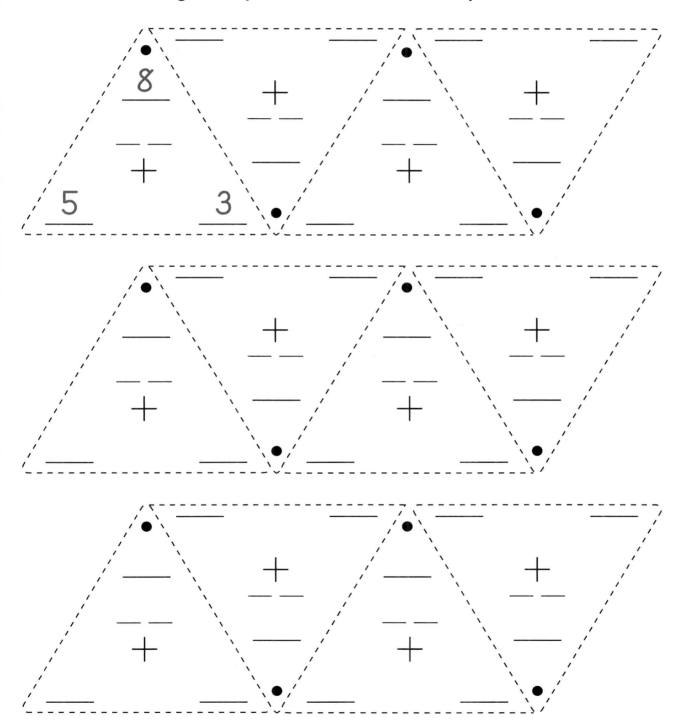

Fraction Circles

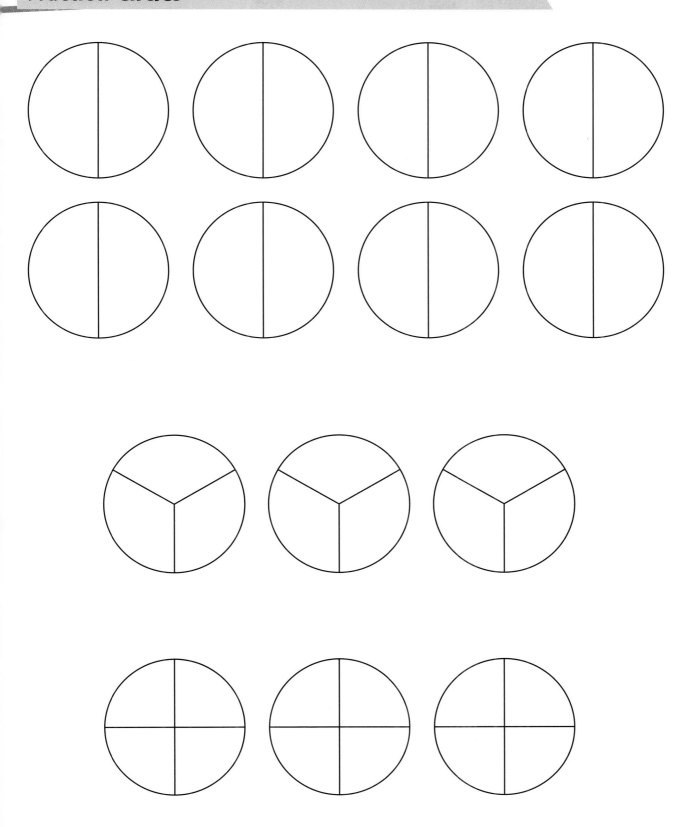

Horizontal Bar Graph

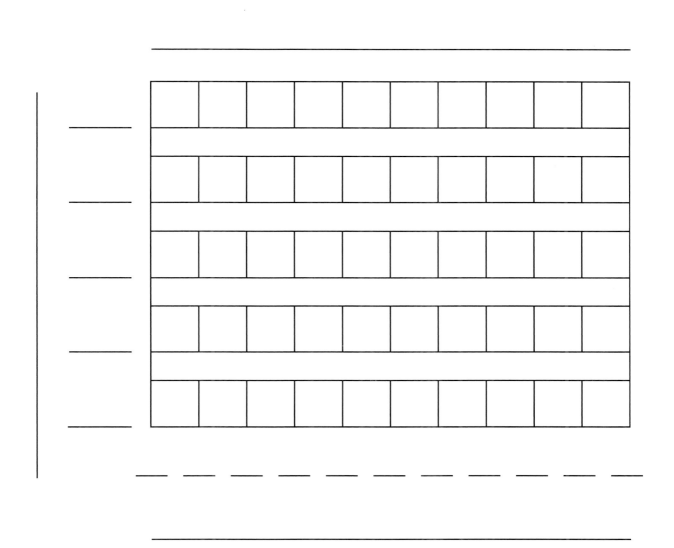

Hundred Chart

1	2	3	4	5	6	7	8	9	10
11	12	13	14	15	16	17	18	19	20
21	22	23	24	25	26	27	28	29	30
31	32	33	34	35	36	37	38	39	40
41	42	43	44	45	46	47	48	49	50
51	52	53	54	55	56	57	58	59	60
61	62	63	64	65	66	67	68	69	70
71	72	73	74	75	76	77	78	79	80
81	82	83	84	85	86	87	88	89	90
91	92	93	94	95	96	97	98	99	100

Hundred Grid

Inch Grid Paper

Multiplication Facts Chart

×	0	1	2	3	4	5	6	7	8	9	10
10											
9											
8											
7											
6											
5											
4											
3											
2											
1											
0											

My Story Problems

Write a story problem on the lines below. Write a number sentence to go with each story problem. Use the space in the large box to work out each problem.

Story Problem 1

_____

_____

_____

_____

____ ☐ ____ ☐ ____

Number sentence

Story Problem 2

_____

_____

_____

_____

____ ☐ ____ ☐ ____

Number sentence

Number line 1 (halves): 0, $\frac{1}{2}$, 1 ($\frac{2}{2}$), $\frac{3}{2}$, 2 ($\frac{4}{2}$)

Number line 2 (thirds): 0, $\frac{1}{3}$, $\frac{2}{3}$, 1 ($\frac{3}{3}$), $\frac{4}{3}$, $\frac{5}{3}$, 2 ($\frac{6}{3}$)

Number line 3 (fourths): 0, $\frac{1}{4}$, $\frac{2}{4}$, $\frac{3}{4}$, 1 ($\frac{4}{4}$), $\frac{5}{4}$, $\frac{6}{4}$, $\frac{7}{4}$, 2 ($\frac{8}{4}$)

Number line 4 (fifths): 0, $\frac{1}{5}$, $\frac{2}{5}$, $\frac{3}{5}$, $\frac{4}{5}$, 1 ($\frac{5}{5}$), $\frac{6}{5}$, $\frac{7}{5}$, $\frac{8}{5}$, $\frac{9}{5}$, 2 ($\frac{10}{5}$)

Number line 5 (sixths): 0, $\frac{1}{6}$, $\frac{2}{6}$, $\frac{3}{6}$, $\frac{4}{6}$, $\frac{5}{6}$, 1 ($\frac{6}{6}$), $\frac{7}{6}$, $\frac{8}{6}$, $\frac{9}{6}$, $\frac{10}{6}$, $\frac{11}{6}$, 2 ($\frac{12}{6}$)

Number line 6 (eighths): 0, $\frac{1}{8}$, $\frac{2}{8}$, $\frac{3}{8}$, $\frac{4}{8}$, $\frac{5}{8}$, $\frac{6}{8}$, $\frac{7}{8}$, 1 ($\frac{8}{8}$), $\frac{9}{8}$, $\frac{10}{8}$, $\frac{11}{8}$, $\frac{12}{8}$, $\frac{13}{8}$, $\frac{14}{8}$, $\frac{15}{8}$, 2 ($\frac{16}{8}$)

Number line 7 (tenths): 0, $\frac{1}{10}$, $\frac{2}{10}$, $\frac{3}{10}$, $\frac{4}{10}$, $\frac{5}{10}$, $\frac{6}{10}$, $\frac{7}{10}$, $\frac{8}{10}$, $\frac{9}{10}$, 1 ($\frac{10}{10}$), $\frac{11}{10}$, $\frac{12}{10}$, $\frac{13}{10}$, $\frac{14}{10}$, $\frac{15}{10}$, $\frac{16}{10}$, $\frac{17}{10}$, $\frac{18}{10}$, $\frac{19}{10}$, 2 ($\frac{20}{10}$)

Number Line 0-20

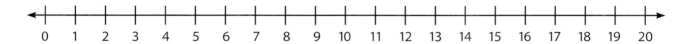

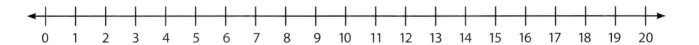

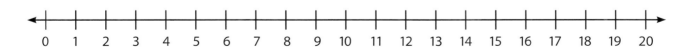

Number Line 0-100

The number lines may be cut out and taped together to form
a number line from 0 to 100.

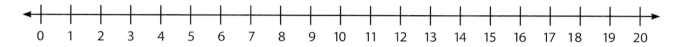

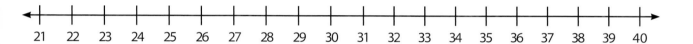

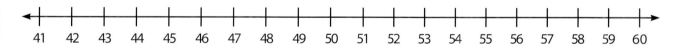

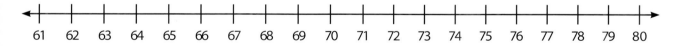

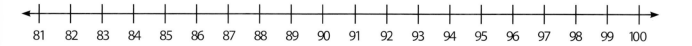

Open Number Lines

Use open number lines to record and keep track of your addition or subtraction strategies.

Example: 48 + 36

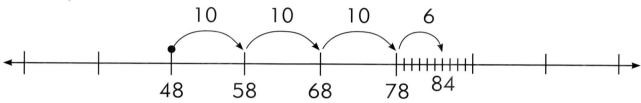

Picture Graph

Each picture in the boxes equals 1.

Place-Value Chart (Hundreds)

Use the blank place-value charts below to solve addition and subtraction problems that use numbers through 500. Use the first column of the chart to write the plus (+) symbol or the minus (−) symbol for each problem.

Here's a sample chart.

	H	T	O
	ı	ı	
	2	7	6
+	2	3	5
	5	ı	ı

	H	T	O

	H	T	O

	H	T	O

	H	T	O

	H	T	O

Place-Value Chart (Thousands)

Use the blank place-value charts below to solve addition and subtraction problems that use numbers through 1,000. Use the first column of the chart to write the plus (+) symbol or the minus (−) symbol for each problem.

Here's a sample chart.

	Th	H	T	O
		I	I	I
		4	6	8
+		5	3	2
	1,	0	0	0

	Th	H	T	O

	Th	H	T	O

	Th	H	T	O

	Th	H	T	O

	Th	H	T	O

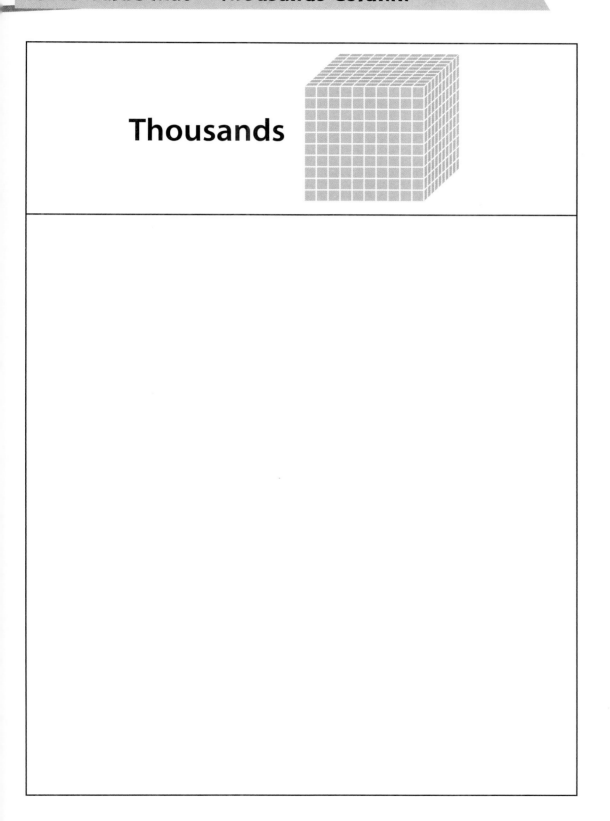

Vertical Bar Graph

Whole to Twelfths Number Lines

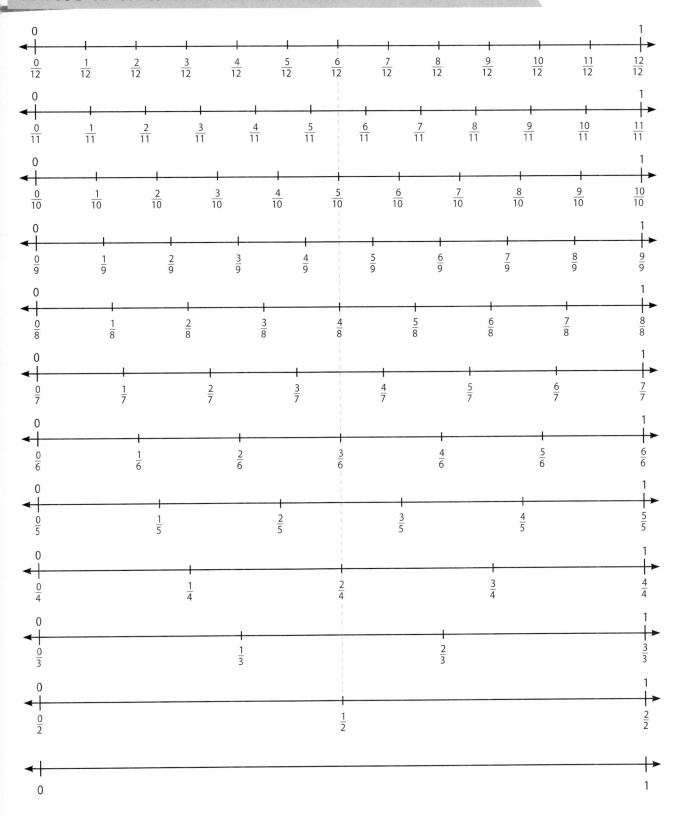